MALCOLM BOYD,

Who was a Guest Fellow at Yale in 1968-69, spends several months each year lecturing on university campuses in the U.S. and Canada. An Episcopal priest, he has long been identified as a leader in the peace movement and civil rights. Best known as author of *Are You Running With Me, Jesus?* he is a playwright, film critic, and has written a number of books. Boston University Library recently established The Malcolm Boyd Collection, a permanent archive of the priest writer's letters and papers. Malcolm Boyd has given readings-in-concert of his written works, accompanied by such musicians as Charlie Byrd, the guitarist; Peter Yarrow of Peter, Paul and Mary; and Oscar Brown, Jr., the composer-star of *Joy.*

"A smashing iconoclast!"
                    Look Magazine

THE FANTASY WORLDS OF PETER STONE
AND OTHER FABLES

MALCOLM BOYD

AVON
PUBLISHERS OF
DISCUS • CAMELOT • BARD

AVON BOOKS
A division of
The Hearst Corporation
959 Eighth Avenue
New York, New York 10019

First Avon Printing, May, 1971

AVON TRADEMARK REG. U.S. PAT. OFF. AND
FOREIGN COUNTRIES, REGISTERED TRADEMARK—
MARCA REGISTRADA, HECHO EN CHICAGO, U.S.A.

Printed in the U.S.A.

CONTENTS

[1]

The Fantasy Worlds
of Peter Stone

He was now Jesus as well as Peter Stone. This warred against his imagination.

Peter had to let it rest. He could not bear to think about the endless images of Jesus, *and* Peter Stone, which were mixed up in millions of people's minds.

"Silent Night." Listening to it, Peter cried. Since he was a child he always had. Now it was Christmas Eve again. In an hour, he would be seen by fifty million Americans on nation-wide television. It frightened as well as exhilarated him.

"Holy infant so tender and mild. . . ." Peter thought of his boyhood. He hadn't minded being a minister's son, although it cost him some ridicule and limited the number of close friends he had. The Stone household had been a strict one.

❧

Peter's father was a Southern Baptist minister who felt it was sinful for a person to smoke, swear, or take a drink.

It was terrible for Peter when his father died. Why, he wondered, had God *done* this? But he decided, even at that early age, never to question God's wisdom. God had done it, and that was that.

Peter remembered the day he had told his mother he would study for the ministry. He was called to this. He must follow in his father's footsteps, and Jesus'.

All through school, *that* was settled and Peter simply prepared for it. He was an exemplary student in Sunday School, sang in the children's choir until his voice changed, and, during high school, assisted the minister by teaching younger boys about the Bible and God, the Church and Jesus. Peter loved these activities very much.

When the minister stood in the pulpit on Sunday mornings, the lights in the church dim with just a spot shining on him, and the people waiting expectantly to hear the Word of God, Peter always felt anticipation and exultation. The minister's voice seemed like great sounds coming out of an organ, beginning softly and easily, swelling in feeling, reaching heights of passion, then ending on a positively dramatic note which sustained and fulfilled all that had gone before.

❧

In Peter's small town, Baptists thought Catholics were anti-Christ. Nuns and priests lived in sin in rectory basements—so the stories went. The basements were filled with ammunition and guns, it was rumored; Catholic priests (God forbid) smoked, swore, and drank; Catholic churches were pagan temples; the altar was magic, and unholy candles flickered inside the church day and night. Visions of these things terrified Peter.

In his early teens Peter went away to a big youth convention in St. Louis. He had never been away from home before. The whole world seemed to open up and make him dizzy. And a new close friend took him to a Catholic church. He shook hands with a priest. The priest laughed and didn't hurt Peter. He met a nun. She was dressed in a long black robe and Peter nearly cried out in fear. But she smiled and put her arm around him. She didn't hurt him, either. Peter slowly walked around the church, running his hands over some stations of the cross. Gradually the numbing fright left him. To his amazement, he found the church the most beautiful place he had ever seen. He lighted a votive candle for his father.

When he returned home, Peter could not mention this experience to anyone. He knew that he could never hurt his mother by telling her about it. However, when Peter was sent off to college, he

found himself in the midst of a great state university. He could lose himself in new experiences and
feel free.

He often became angry. Christianity was true
and had to be believed and accepted by faith alone.
Why did his professors attack faith, ridiculing it
and extolling logical proofs? There could be no
proofs of God! Yet he sometimes felt himself losing God. At such times he hated himself.

Peter found the Catholic chapel. No one from
the Southern Baptist group ever visited it. This
provided necessary secrecy for Peter's daily visit
to early Mass. The altar. *God's* altar. It was so
high—up, up there with the six blinding candles
on candelabra and great bronze vases of holy
flowers. In front of the altar Peter could scarcely
get his breath. *This was holy.* One day he went
with everybody else up to the altar to receive the
holy communion. He closed his eyes. A priest
placed the bread, the spiritual body of Jesus, *in
his mouth and he ate it.* For a moment, until he
swallowed it, he was holy too. It burned in his
throat. He did not dare taste it, for what if a
miracle occurred and it were real flesh and not
only spiritual? He feared that he would vomit or
faint, and maybe be struck dead by God.

Not able to bear the awful intensity of this,

Peter was relieved, yet sad, to leave the presence of God. He knew he would be back again the next morning. Meanwhile there was life to be endured and lived.

He wrestled with things of the flesh. He knew that he must put sex, with Satan, away from him. Once, after a period of weakness when he had had sexual relations with a girl he dated on campus, he felt fallen from grace. He was stained by filth. He was unworthy to stand in the holy presence of God.

That night he stayed in the church, prostrated on the stone floor before the altar, his arms outstretched as Jesus' arms had been on the cross. Only Jesus had been nailed to the holy wood when Jesus died for all men, including Peter, on the cross. Jesus died for him and he was ungrateful, faithless, and impure. Peter thought of St. Peter trying to walk on the water. Oh, Lord, sustain me, he cried within himself. "The devil, as a roaring lion, walketh about, seeking whom he may devour." Tears ran down Peter's face as he lay on the cold stone floor.

After that Peter stood firmly against Satan. He did not kiss a girl again in college. He would be a Southern Baptist minister with the celibate fervor of a Catholic priest. Peter would be *God's* man.

∾

And on Sunday mornings, during the Baptist service as the mighty hymns of the Church sounded triumphantly, he felt he could not wait for his service in the Kingdom to begin.

At last it did. Peter entered seminary to immerse himself in the religious life. Thank God, Peter thought, the world was *out there,* with its filth, temptations, and false values. Peter was grateful to be always with God inside the very high stone walls, theological structures, and devotional practices of the seminary.

There was a brief period of protest and revolt when Peter was in the seminary. Two young assistant professors, who had got mixed up in civil rights and peace, stirred up nine students to fight for "academic freedom" and "seminary power." Peter was glad he could play a leading role in defeating the movement which led to the expulsion of everybody involved. They had not apparently realized that Christianity is concerned with spiritual, not temporal, matters; the soul, not the body; the Kingdom of God, not the world.

Then, in Peter's third year of theological training in the seminary, his whole life changed abruptly. He would never again be the same.

Aldono Forminelli had announced his plans to make a $20,000,000 film entitled *Jesus.* A worldwide search was announced to find "an unknown actor" for the role of Jesus. Lately, the search had centered on seminaries.

At the time of his first interview with a talent scout from Hollywood who visited the seminary, Peter had scarcely given the matter a second thought. In fact, he considered it altogether remote and utterly impossible.

Later Forminelli himself flew to the seminary to interview Peter.

"It's remarkable," Forminelli told him. "You *look* like Jesus. Did anyone ever tell you you did?"

"How do you know, sir, how Jesus looked?" Peter asked him, not without indignation tinged with pity.

Forminelli laughed, throwing his head back with the earthy insolence of a successful peasant.

"Have you thought, Mr. Stone, how Jesus acted as a man in everyday life?" Forminelli asked.

"Don't forget, Mr. Forminelli," Peter said, "that Jesus was not only a man in everyday life. He was also completely divine."

Forminelli liked Peter's earnest sincerity, even his apparent lack of a sense of humor. There seemed to be no guile or taint of opportunism in the young seminarian. Success should not spoil him.

The choice had narrowed to a competition be-

❧

tween a young Yugoslavian actor, a seminarian in Rome, and Peter. When Peter was finally offered the role, church leaders were drawn into negotiations. Along with the head of the seminary, they were unanimous in urging Peter to accept. "It is an unprecedented opportunity to preach the gospel by portraying Jesus Christ before millions of people throughout the world," a church leader said. "Think of it. Jews and Moslems, Hindus and Buddhists, atheists and mere humanists, will all be confronted by Christ. And a Southern Baptist seminarian will portray Him! This is truly a blessing from God. I have prayed about this and feel it is surely God's will that you accept."

When Peter did, there was a service of leavetaking, to ask God's guidance for him, in the seminary chapel.

"Go in faith," the preacher said in the service. "Go out from this place in pure Abrahamitic faith. You will portray our Lord on the screen. Go in the faith of Him who always moved in faith."

Peter was to catch a plane for Hollywood. His fellow seminarians lined up to say good-by. In his heart, Peter swore that he would not be corrupted but would return. After the plane took off, he wanted to read the New Testament. Yet he had his script to learn.

Initial shooting of the film would take place in Hollywood before it shifted to locations in various parts of the world. Significantly, only half of *Jesus* would be filmed in a historic and biblical context. The second half would be shot in modern dress and contemporary locations. The screenplay depicted Jesus, during the latter part of the picture, as being present in nine different situations involving people and their problems. In one, Jesus would be seen as a member of a labor union; in others, a Peace Corps volunteer, a stockbroker, a black militant, a Vietnamese soldier, a French statesman, a schoolteacher, a vice-president of the United States, and a priest.

Aldono Forminelli fascinated Peter almost as much as Peter fascinated Forminelli. At first they could only reach out to one another quite tentatively. Each wondered what really motivated the other. Peter felt Forminelli was being used as God's instrument to make the picture, yet he felt confident that the producer was unaware of providence. Forminelli was convinced that Peter felt called by God to portray Jesus in the film, and seriously pondered if Peter were half-mad or lost in sexually activated religious hallucinations. Underneath such feelings, each liked the other.

Forminelli, the son of an Italian peasant, had

forced his way to wealth and international prestige. Now married to Lucia Perizzi, he had established her as a ranking box-office star (she would play a cameo role as Magdalene in *Jesus*.) He had amassed a vast personal fortune, accumulating two castles—one in Bavaria, the other in Ireland —along with a Greek yacht well known to the Jet Set, a skiing haven in Gstaad, a New York town house, and a place in Palm Springs where he had acted as host to two U.S. presidents. He was living in a bungalow at a Beverly Hills hotel during the shooting of *Jesus*.

Peter occupied another bungalow at the same hotel. His meals were with people also working on the film and were catered by hotel room service, to be eaten in his bungalow or Forminelli's. Peter needed a car; he was given a new Mercedes. Peter was seldom seen in public. It was generally assumed that, after the film had been completed, he would return to seminary and continue his theological studies. Meanwhile, his salary ($2,000 a week) was deposited for him in a bank account and his living expenses paid by the studio.

"Don't misunderstand what I am doing," Forminelli told his publicity director. "This *is*, despite appearances, a biblical spectacular. I'm deliberately throwing the critics and public off guard by utilizing modern situations and locations in half the picture. But, from beginning to end, the production itself will be that of a biblical spectacular.

"Peter Stone will be permitted to grant, at the most, a half-dozen press interviews during the shooting. When that's finished, we'll send him on a three-month world-wide publicity tour.

"While we're in production, he will live, eat, and sleep either on the set itself or in his hotel bungalow near me. When we're on location, it will be the same. Your main job will be to keep a close watch over him at all times. Don't let people get to him. We want to build up almost a feeling of holiness and transcendent aloofness about him. No one must ever forget that he is playing *Jesus Christ*.

"Then, when the movie is released, the shock of a modern, human Jesus will be all the more pronounced because of our earlier secrecy and mystery. Then we'll really spring Peter Stone on the world. I've got him tied up for his next three pictures. Don't ever, *ever*, mention this to him or anybody else.

"I personally selected you because I noticed the press job you did on the Moses spectacular two years ago. I liked it. Only this job is going to be

more sophisticated and challenging for you.
Trickier. Tougher. We don't want newspaper and
magazine space *first*, remember. The same applies
to TV or radio exploitation. We want mystery.
We want the creation of illusion. We want the
whole world to care about this film. I expect the
highest grosses in the history of motion pictures.''

The first scene to be photographed on the Hollywood set in which Peter appeared was one depicting Jesus walking with a group of his disciples.
Looking at the rushes, Forminelli observed a
strength he had not previously acknowledged in
Peter. To the portrayal of Jesus he brought a
sense of motivation and inner power. The word
was out that Peter Stone would be an important
star when *Jesus* was released.

Tyle Alcutt was directing *Jesus*. His relationship with Peter was very tenuous for the first
three weeks of shooting. Part of the time Peter
passively accepted direction. Then, without warning, he would flare up on the set, rejecting Alcutt's
interpretation. After this he would sometimes remain hidden in his feelings for days. At these
times filming was a tedious, edgy process and
communication was fragmented.

Tension had built up unbearably when the
Lazarus sequence was to be filmed.

❧

"Now, Peter, I want you to play this with dignity and power," Alcutt told him. "I see real majesty here. You're going to perform the greatest miracle of your life."

Peter didn't answer. He seemed tied up in knots of silence within himself.

"Damn it, Peter, give a little," Alcutt shouted at him. "Give. Aren't you human, man? Talk to me. Talk. Give. If you can't talk to me, Peter, I'm walking off this picture and I'll never come back. I can't work with some kind of a divine machine, man."

A hush had fallen on the set. Peter looked at Alcutt for a moment. Then he spoke very quietly and there did not seem to be any anger or hostility in his manner.

"Tyle, I know how you feel and I'm sorry. This is tough for me, too, Tyle." A look of relaxation came into Alcutt's eyes. "Let me try it my way first, will you, Tyle?"

"Sure, Peter. Sure. How do you want to do it?"

"I'll show you, Tyle. I want to do it quietly. Very slow and easy, Tyle, without any phony dignity or anything like that."

As the Lazarus sequence was filmed, tough members of the crew were seen to have wet eyes. After this, Alcutt trusted Peter. He didn't give Peter all the rope but he let him lead. Portraying

Jesus seemed, to Peter, a natural and easy thing to do. He had a definite sense about it. He was happiest when the cameras were rolling and he was involved, as Jesus, in historical or modern life situations. The hardest times were when he had to be Peter Stone again. Forminelli was the first to spot this, although it was only intuitively. Considerably later Tyle Alcutt came to realize it.

Peter loved the episode with Mary Magdalene. Lucia Perizzi played the part very well, he thought. She came to him in her beauty and pride, also her degradation and overwhelming sin, and he forgave her. He healed her. No longer would she cast away her life on corruptible things of the flesh and the world.

Peter dined that night with Forminelli and Lucia. One of the world's reigning beauties, she was in a relaxed and generous mood.

"Peter, darling, you were fabulous," she said.

"This was one of my favorite scenes in the film," he told her.

"Sweet. You're sweet. You were positively sexy, darling, I don't know how else to say it. You played this with tenderness and compassion, Peter, but you also came through as a very sexy man. I loved it, darling. You gave strength and love and sex to *me*."

THE FANTASY WORLDS
OF PETER STONE

Peter excused himself soon after dinner. Lucia
flew to Rome in a day or so to start her new film
there. Forminelli and Peter never mentioned the
incident. Instead of giving Peter confidence, it
shattered him. However, after several days
Peter's composure returned and soon afterward
his apparent inner strength. Forminelli marveled.

Peter felt great camaraderie playing Jesus with
the disciples. They followed, obeyed, and *loved*
him. Peter interpreted the miracles with excep-
tional grace and charm, the crew thought. He was
not heavyhanded and somehow took them for
granted. And, in the scenes depicting Jesus on the
cross, an unnatural, chilling stillness spread
across the set. The words uttered from the cross
caught fire, came to real life, and seemed to cut
their way through religious cant.

Forminelli's secrecy began paying off for him
in publicity. Headlines stressed it. "Why Secrecy
on $20,000,000 'Jesus'?" "'Jesus' Set Tighter
Than Drum." "Controversy Rages Over 'Jesus'
Film." Two hundred thousand photographs of
Peter in the role of Jesus (in historical costume)
were requested by the Youth Department of a
major U.S. denomination for distribution to youth
throughout the country. However, in instance
after instance, requests for press interviews with

❧

Peter were turned down by Forminelli's publicity staff. Every precaution was taken to avoid overexposure of Peter before the film's release.

A brilliant woman journalist was made an exception by being granted an interview. It was an assignment from one of the leading magazines. The interview took place on the side of a reconstructed Jerusalem street. Accompanied by a press agent (who had formerly worked as executive secretary for a Bishop), they sat on stone steps. The journalist asked permission to smoke and it was given.

"Have you been more influenced by the Synoptics or by the Fourth Gospel?" she asked.

"Oh, the Synoptics," Peter replied. "I suppose more by Luke than the other gospels."

"Do you think Jesus was homosexual, Mr. Stone?"

"I feel that Jesus' sexuality transcended all human categories," he replied. "Yet it encompassed an awareness and understanding—even something deeper, an involvement in the whole spectrum of what we call sex. And without sin. He remained sinless."

"I know this sounds like a terribly academic question, Mr. Stone," she continued, smiling and shaking her famous tawny hair, "but what *is* sin?'' She coughed her celebrated cough, known to the nation because she was seen weekly on the television program *Press Conference*. She fixed him in her gaze. ''I mean, *really,* you know, what is it?''

''Sin is separation from God.''

''*Can* one be, well, *separated* from God, Mr. Stone, if indeed God is everywhere?''

''Oh, yes, because of one's free will. One may reject or accept God.''

''Fascinating.'' She flipped through her pages of notes. ''And are you returning to seminary, after this?''—she gestured with her hand to the set—''or will you become a star, Mr. Stone?''

''I expect to return to the seminary.''

''Forgive my candor, I don't in any sense wish to appear to be rude but I'm sure you realize you give the figure of Jesus a contemporaneity, even, one might say, a definition of bold human masculinity. You're sexy to women, Mr. Stone. Do you feel you *ought* to be? Your face, your body, *shouldn't* they be less *attractive?*''

''Jesus was completely human as well as completely divine. He was a real man. A total man. Surely he neither exaggerated nor diminished his manhood. He was, I should think, unself-conscious about it.''

"*I see.*" She was hurriedly jotting down his words in her note pad. "And I do want to *thank* you, Mr. Stone. You've been absolutely charming."

Protected for the most part from press and public, Peter maintained a very simple existence between the hotel and the set. He met an early morning makeup call, worked hard all day, then studied the next day's script in the evenings, and went to bed right after looking at the 11 P.M. television news. When the film went on location, Peter's life still remained simple and functional. Location shooting started in Israel, then moved to Spain, England, France, and Italy. Already Peter was a celebrity. A full-time secretary was required to handle his fan mail, even though the public had not yet seen him on the screen.

As he grew in the role, Peter matured. He grew as a man before other men's eyes. Forminelli saw that the humanness he possessed was warm, compassionate, and marked by an inner authority he seemed to have no need of justifying. Yet Forminelli sensed that at the core Peter was flawed by inner insecurity and a curious lack of self-identity.

In foreign countries Peter became something of a hero. Yet, to Forminelli's amazement, Peter refused to capitalize on it. Forminelli had become

quite fond of Peter but Peter was increasingly a
mystery to him. He knew that Peter lived the
private life of a recluse. What did Peter *want?* In
fact, who was this man Peter?

The final scene was photographed late one night
on a near-empty Hollywood set. People shook
Peter's hand, assured him that he had been mag-
nificent, drank a cup of coffee, and went home to
their families. It was finished.

Between the time he finished dubbing and re-
shooting, and the release of the film, Peter was at
loose ends. He returned to Europe, traveling to
Chartres, St. Peter's, St. Mark's in Venice, West-
minster Abbey, Fatima, the Patriarchate in Con-
stantinople (he refused to call it Istanbul),
Mount Athos, and thence to Jerusalem. Later,
back in the U.S., he visited his seminary for a
week. Then he made an ecumenical tour of some
sixty seminaries. Soon there were magazine interviews to give, appearances to be made at church
conventions, and a head-on confrontation with
celebrity.

When *Jesus* opened in New York, church leaders mixed with the world of society, fashion, and
communications for the gala benefit world pre-
miere. Peter attended it with Forminelli. When
the film ended Peter received an ovation. Women

wept openly and a spirit of adulation seized the audience which seemed to take Peter into its collective arms.

During the showing of the picture, Peter felt a sense of well-being and security. Life was happening *up there* and he was a part of it. But when the lights came up inside the theater, that life abruptly ended, and his own was suddenly reduced to people in a mob smiling at him and trying to grab his hands. He felt dead.

That night, he sat up late with Forminelli.

"I don't know what to say to you, Peter. I'm proud of you. I'm proud of you, Peter."

Peter fingered his glass and didn't reply.

"Peter, the whole world's at your feet, boy," Forminelli went on. "Don't you want this? Isn't this what you wanted?"

"I don't know what to say or do, Aldo," Peter told him. "I wish I could see ahead."

"I'll do anything you want, Peter," Forminelli said. "You can go straight back to the seminary if you want. I don't care. I want to do whatever will make you happy."

"Happy?" Peter laughed, then grew quiet again. "Seminary is a fantasy world in the past, Aldo. It seems like a nice religious drama which I remember seeing in a church a long time ago. I can't ever go back to it. I have to be me and live my life."

"Who are you, Peter?"

"Good Aldo," Peter said, laughing again. "I might as well say who are you, Aldo? And you don't see anything funny about that."

A silence fell between them.

"Yes. Yes, Peter," Forminelli replied. "I see what is both funny and unfunny about that."

"You see, Aldo, I am simply myself. You brought me into this situation. It made me happy and gave me a sense of fulfillment on the basis of the self I was. Now the present, the immediacy, you gave me is ended. I can't go back. I can't stand still. And I don't know where to go."

"What makes you so different, then, Peter?"

"Ah, Aldo. I can't win with you. All right. I accept the universality of problems, but my own remains."

"Doesn't your Jesus Christ help you, Peter? I have never discussed this with you. Now I feel I have the right or at least I must, for I care about you. What about your Jesus? Where is he? Is he with you, Peter?"

"Aldo, I can't talk about it."

"Why can't you talk about it?"

"I have to unlearn a lot, Aldo. I am close to

Jesus but not to religion now. I have searching to
do. Maybe one doesn't need to bring Jesus any-
where. Maybe Jesus is already there. I don't
know, Aldo. I'm trying to sort things out.''

Peter still had a three-month promotional tour,
which would take him around the world. Forminelli assigned three press representatives to accompany him, warning them to preserve Peter's
privacy wherever possible. Yet it was an occasion
of almost total exposure. Peter flew to Boston,
then Washington, Atlanta, Philadelphia, Cleveland, Pittsburgh, Detroit, Chicago, St. Louis, Den-
ver, San Francisco, and Los Angeles. After this
he set out on his flying trip circling the world.
Everywhere he met the press, spoke with church
leaders, and appeared on television and radio.

''When I see you I *feel* Jesus is near me,'' an
English duchess told him. ''You have made Jesus
a man I can relate to as a human being,'' said a
member of the Ghanian government. ''I believe
you must truly understand Jesus as no other man
can,'' a journalist in Buenos Aires told Peter. ''I
mistrust Hollywood and America and the movie
and you, but somehow your Jesus is real,'' said a
student leader in India. Peter's face was as well
known as Mao's, his voice as Aretha Franklin's.
He was asked to write books on theology. He had

preached in the great cathedrals of the world.
People wrote to him for advice about prayer,
marriage problems, politics, race, poverty, and
war.

Now, the tour had nearly come to an end. Back
in New York, it was Christmas Eve. Peter was
seated in a dressing room in a television studio. In
an hour he would portray Jesus in a short scene
for fifty million Americans across the country.

Instead of appearing on the television program
he wanted to go away with Jesus, now, in this
moment. Somehow he knew he had instead to stay
with Jesus here. But he couldn't play Jesus anymore. He would have to be Peter. Someone was
singing "Silent Night."

෴

2

Samuel Joseph
for President

The presidential jet was flying from Washington, D.C. to Los Angeles. Inside it, his coat off and sleeves rolled up, the president of the United States was in conference with a group of key advisers.

"It looks far worse than I had any idea it could, Ron," the president said to one of his intimate aides. "What can we do?"

"I don't know, Mr. President," Ron Dixon replied. "It looks very bad indeed. I'm stumped. If I could have a day or so to think about it, I might be able to come up with something."

"Unfortunately, I've got to know exactly what to do the minute I get off the plane in Los Angeles," the president said. "I'll be riding with Anderson in the car from the airport to my hotel.

That's when I've got to talk with him about it.''

The presidential advisers looked at one another uneasily. Two of them put out their cigarettes, two others lit cigarettes, and one stoked his pipe. Fresh coffee was poured.

One of the younger aides in the group spoke up.

''Mr. President, it's no secret now that Anderson is losing the election.'' He pulled out sheafs of paper. ''Look. Here are breakdowns on all the latest polls. You've seen them. Unless something drastic can be done in the next three weeks, he hasn't got a chance.''

This direct confrontation with the commonly known, but forbidden subject, took the lid off a growing and unbearable tension.

''If that's true, then my eight years as president will be repudiated when my party goes down to defeat with Anderson in November.'' The president shifted in his chair. He brought down his fist on the table. ''I'll fight. I'm willing to fight, do anything, to prevent that from happening.''

The young aide persisted in his line of reasoning, looking the president squarely in the eye.

''We've checked and rechecked every conceivable angle in this election, sir,'' he continued. ''There doesn't seem to be any area of flexibility where we can safely introduce a new angle or exploit an old one. We're stalemated on peace, race, poverty, health, urban development, air pollution, the space program.'' He held up a finger of his hand to emphasize each item he was ticking off. ''Mr. President, we're in the worst possible trouble.''

Blocked by frustration, the president was visibly growing angry.

''I think I've got an idea,'' Ron Dixon said.

He leaned forward in his chair, holding in check his excitement.

''There's one area we might be able to maneuver in. I'm not saying it would be easy. It's difficult and explosive. But religion could make the difference and throw the election to Anderson if we handle it right and keep our heads.''

The president was displeased.

''Damn it, Ron, you *never* mix religion and politics. Rule one. Have you lost your mind? This situation is serious. Can't we be serious too?''

Ron Dixon smiled.

''You mix oil and water if you have to, to survive, Mr. President.'' He was cool and seemed quite confident of himself. ''Religion is an untapped political resource in this election. The church is unpopular but God isn't. Nobody knows how to define God but most people believe in a God. Now, as to *this* election. Anderson is running against a Jew. The first Jew to run for president. Samuel Joseph.''

A sudden interest gripped everybody seated around the table.

''Anti-Semitism seems to be over, at least on the surface. Nobody in his right mind would dig it up. In fact, you have to appear liberal about a Jew running for president. Anderson has been very good about that. So have you, Mr. President. And America is saying we've-had-our-Catholic, now-let's-have-our-Jew. Okay. But now I come to my point. Samuel Joseph isn't mentioning religion. He's a Jew, and that's that, but Jewishness is not being brought up by *any*body. This leaves a vacuum in the election for religion. Why doesn't Anderson bring up religion? Not negatively. Not in any sense against, or related to, Joseph. But positively. Positively for Anderson.''

The others could tell the president was excited by the power of this new idea. ''You may have something, Dixon,'' he said, leaning back and lighting his pipe. ''You may really have something. What you seem to be saying is, Anderson should get religion. God is not dead, he's in conference with Philip Anderson.''

Everybody laughed.

"All right. How do we implement this? You tell me we've got three weeks at the most to change the course of this election. Wouldn't you think we should get started on it today?''

Ideas were shot back and forth across the table.

"I think it might work,'' one adviser said. "But the public must be told Anderson isn't discovering religion three weeks before the election. He's had it all along. He didn't want to exploit it. That cut against the grain of his integrity and humility. But something must happen to force him to open up on religion. You know, he must do this according to the dictates of his conscience.''

"Couldn't Anderson have prayed about this for a long time?'' Dixon asked. "Now he believes it is God's will for him to speak about religion because of the immorality of the nation.''

"Man cannot cope with the problem by himself,'' another aide suggested. "Phil Anderson suddenly realizes the peril in which the nation stands. Only God can make the difference. You know, between disaster and what might be called a new morality.''

"I like it," said the president. "Put your heads together. Come up with some kind of a definite program. I can give it to Anderson when I'm riding in the car with him from the airport. There's just no time to lose."

At the airport, the president spoke briefly to an army of TV, radio, and press correspondents. Anderson, bareheaded and smiling, stood next to the president. Then the two men got into a limousine and a police escort started them on their way to the gigantic political rally.

"I'm worried," Anderson told the president. "I seem to have hit a slump and can't pull myself up again."

"Don't worry, Phil." The president laughed. Anderson sensed his confidence. "I've got an idea. If you agree, I think it might just do the job."

That night Ron Dixon put in a long-distance call to Ellsworth Pinkney, who agreed to meet Anderson and Dixon the next day in Kansas City. Pinkney was one of the most influential magazine editors in the country, an elder statesman of contemporary Protestantism, and a party stalwart. He would be told nothing about political strategy, only that Anderson's conscience made it necessary for him to speak out boldly concerning the state of the nation's morality and how God must be given the reins of action.

At noon the next day, Pinkney had lunch with Anderson and Dixon in Kansas City where Anderson was to speak in the evening at a political rally.

"Of course, I'm delighted, even, I must say, quite thrilled, Mr. Anderson, to find out your real feelings," Pinkney said. "But I also must confess that I'm puzzled by your previous silence on the subject of religion. You haven't, to my knowledge, said anything at all about it. Nor have I been aware that you even attended church services on Sundays during the campaign."

"You see, Dr. Pinkney, I feel very strongly about the separation of church and state," Anderson replied. "And, too, I've leaned over backward, I can tell you confidentially, not to raise the subject of religion because I thought it might prove to be politically embarrassing for Mr. Joseph."

Pinkney sipped his glass of milk.

"I see," he commented. "I see. Well, Mr. Anderson, I certainly respect you deeply for what you have done."

Anderson folded his hands together on the table.

"But I can't keep religion out anymore," Anderson announced. "I can't try to keep God out of the election anymore, Dr. Pinkney. And, frankly, I just don't care if it hurts me or not, even if it should cost me the election, because the issue is basic now for our very survival as a Christian nation. I suppose I should say as a religious nation."

"No, I see nothing wrong with acknowledging our destiny under God as a Christian nation, Mr. Anderson." Pinkney paused. "How can I be of immediate help to you? I'm quite aware that our time is fast running out."

"We need your thinking, Dr. Pinkney," Ron Dixon replied. "Your ideas on how we can best communicate Mr. Anderson's deep feelings to the nation as rapidly as possible."

Pinkney took a small black leather notebook out of his coat pocket and started to make some notations in it.

"First, you must make a major statement of your viewpoint. Where will you be speaking tomorrow night?"

"In Cleveland."

"Excellent. I'll work with you on drafting your statement. It should be made tomorrow night in Cleveland. In addition, I'll see if something can't be worked out on television over the weekend. There's to be an important TV special on religion in America. Perhaps you've heard about it. I just might be able to get you a spot on that. And, of course, I'll have to get you and Bruce Whippick together as quickly as possible."

Ron Dixon relaxed inside. It was going to be all right. Bruce Whippick was known as "the ad man's revivalist" and was one of the most loved and trusted men in American life. If these new plans could get rolling quickly enough, Dixon thought, Anderson might damned well have an excellent chance of reversing the tide.

Cleveland, the next day, was friendly to Anderson. The largest crowd of the campaign greeted his motorcade. The networks planned to cover his address that night.

The auditorium was packed to the rafters when Anderson mounted the podium to speak. After deafening applause, there was suddenly total stillness inside the great hall.

"My fellow Americans," Anderson began, "I have reached a momentous decision after considerable soul-searching and spiritual anguish." It seemed that nobody breathed among the thousands seated before him. "Up to this time I have painstakingly endeavored to eliminate a great factor, indeed the greatest factor of all, from my campaign. I can do so no longer.

"Our great and beloved nation is pressed on all sides by forces of godless communism abroad and by the decadent and corrupt forces of pagan immorality at home. As men and women, we cannot win our battles against these enemies alone. We must humbly and prayerfully turn to our great Father. We must now, as faithful children, ask God to bring us through to victory abroad and morality and love at home."

For a long, sustained moment there was only silence. Dixon counted to three, wondering what might happen. Then a groundswell of applause started on the auditorium floor. Like fire, it spread to the balconies. On all sides, people seemed to respond to a primordial vision embedded deep within themselves. Now the crowd was on its feet, shouting and swaying. Someone started an old gospel hymn. Men and women were openly and unabashedly crying. Underneath layers of sophistication and cynicism, a terrible need had been touched.

For twenty full minutes, Anderson could not go on with his prepared address as the people inside the auditorium were unrestrained in their emotional response. Finally he was able to continue.

❧

"I was ashamed of my religion. I thought that politics required of me that I should not speak about my God. I am ashamed no longer. We are one nation, indivisible, under God. In God we trust. America is the most Christian, the most religious nation in the history of the world.

"We have a destiny. It is a holy destiny and we are a holy people. We are truly called by God to be his instruments of peace, love, and morality in the world. We must cast down the pagan idols of immorality. We must burn those things which are filthy and degrading to our holiness. We must oppose all things, all ideologies, which are godless. My fellow Americans, I pledge myself to the task of setting this nation on a mighty forward march with God."

Again and again, his speech was interrupted by applause, shouts, and cries of encouragement and support. When he left the podium, tears in his eyes, the thousands stood in an ovation which stirred the nation. And then, at just this moment, Bruce Whippick, the revivalist who had become a folk hero in his own time, walked on the stage and to the podium. The crowd went wild once again. "God! God! God!" the people shouted, starting slowly and ending up with a fast locomotive yell.

Whippick spoke very briefly. He promised to be

a part of Anderson's campaign until the election.

"I support Philip Anderson as the candidate for president who promises to put God back into politics. He will place God in the center of American life, my fellow citizens. God will fight for us against godless communism. God will wage our war against the forces of filth and immorality. God will be our leader, at home and abroad, and Philip Anderson will be his faithful servant in the White House and the hearts of his countrymen."

When he had concluded his remarks, Whippick asked a rabbi, who had been flown in from Detroit, to offer the benediction. The people were requested, after that, to file out of the auditorium in silence, offering prayers to God instead of speaking. As the thousands departed, only the sound of shuffling feet could be heard along with old-fashioned hymns played on an organ.

Pinkney was able to get Philip Anderson a major spot on the weekend TV special about religion in America. The network also offered a place on the program to Samuel Joseph, but Joseph declined.

In prime time Sunday night, the television program opened with a cathedral choir singing "The Star-Spangled Banner." During this music, there were camera stills of the American Revolutionary

War, mixed with present-day films of Hawaii beaches, Midwest fields of grain, the Rockies, the nation's Capitol, the metropolis of New York, blooming flowers in the Deep South, Los Angeles freeways, and the sea off the New England coast.

Pilgrims were shown, fleeing religious persecution in England to settle in America. There were location scenes in some famous early churches, with local choirs and clergymen singing and speaking. European persecution of Jews was depicted, along with their exodus to the land of the free and the home of the brave. There were no shots of early American blacks. However, later in the program, two famed black singers were featured in traditional Christmas carols.

After the program showed films depicting drug addiction, urban crime, racial unrest, ghetto poverty, and a home for unwed mothers, Philip Anderson spoke about God and morality. He was televised live, making his remarks from the pulpit of a leading Fifth Avenue church.

"America was founded on obedience to God's laws," he declared. "Just as God freed the people of Israel from the bondage of Egypt only to have them turn their backs on him, so Americans have forgotten the God who fashioned their nation and have likewise turned away. It is our national salvation to return to the great Father who makes all of us brothers to one another. This nation was called into existence by God. In—God—we—trust.''

Immediately following Anderson's remarks, a children's choir of a West Coast cathedral sang ''God Bless America.'' The closing shot was of ten national religious leaders, representing Catholicism, Protestantism, and Judaism, standing in a single line. A cross and a Star of David were revealed behind them and, over their heads, an American flag fluttered in a breeze mechanically induced by electric fans outside camera range.

Attacks followed immediately.

Liberal Catholic and Protestant journals, with very limited circulations, attacked Anderson for indulging in political opportunism and religious huckstering. Segments of the press joined in the attack on ''outrageous chauvinism.'' When Samuel Joseph replied to Anderson, in his next political address, calling for a return to the separation of church and state as an honored American tradition, he was booed. His remarks led to swastikas being painted on synagogues throughout the U.S.

Anderson promptly denounced these ''acts of political demagoguery.''

"God is love," he said in a press statement after a New Jersey synagogue was bombed and the word "God" was scrawled in red paint on a nearby stone wall. "God calls on us to love our enemies as ourselves." He said that his political followers must "obey the law of love."

The campaign was now in a state of chaos. The president had not foreseen these subsequent events and was distressed by them. At the same time, he was pleased to note that the polls, in an abrupt shift, now clearly favored Anderson. When a Supreme Court justice unexpectedly died, the president swiftly replaced him with a Jewish law professor from Seattle.

Reporters delved into Anderson's religious past. He had been confirmed by an Episcopalian Bishop at the age of thirteen. After that, his institutional religious ties were vague. As Anderson's press conferences leaned more and more to the subject of religion, he supported public prayer in the schools, affirmed the active presence of God on America's side in international relations, and called on ghetto blacks in U.S. cities to "follow Jesus' way of love and peace instead of the devil's way of hate and violence."

During a nationally televised debate, both Anderson and Joseph were asked to discuss their religious beliefs. Joseph indicated that he was a practicing adherent of conservative Judaism, with his social ethic based on the teachings of the Torah. Anderson explained that he was "simply ecumenical," believing that God is "the Father of us all." When pressed by Samuel Joseph, he confessed that he personally rejected the long-accepted categories of American religion as Protestant, Catholic, and Jewish. "But I do not wish to impose my views on anyone else. A man's religion is sacred to him and must be so respected by others. It is just that, for me personally, I believe and practice one God, one religion, one Father, and one brotherhood."

As anti-Semitism sharply increased, and religious controversy replaced political campaigning, the president called an emergency meeting at the White House. Philip Anderson was present along with Ellsworth Pinkney and Bruce Whippick.

"I respect your views, Anderson," the president said, "but we're caught in a hornet's nest. Stability must be restored, at whatever cost. Some latent and dangerous feelings have been stirred in the public, I fear, and the situation must be set aright."

"What can I do, Mr. President?" asked Anderson.

"I don't know, Anderson. That's why I've asked you to come here to meet with Dr. Pinkney, Mr. Whippick, and my aides. We must devise a strategy to lead us out of this dilemma."

Pinkney was the first to speak.

"Mr. President, I deplore the controversy and violence as much as you do, sir. But I do not regret the explicit inclusion of God and religion in this political campaign. It has shown me that we are, truly, a godless people headed for destruction unless we are able to come to grips with the presence and sovereignty of God in our lives."

Ron Dixon leaned forward and addressed Pinkney.

"But when you say 'God' in today's American society, what have you said? It seems to mean whatever an individual person wants it to mean. So, for example, if someone says 'In God we trust,' what specifically does he mean by 'God'? I think we're lost in a jungle of conflicting words and images, and it's, pardon me, sir, damned dangerous."

Bruce Whippick spoke next.

"We've always been taught, Mr. President, that things must get worse before they can get better. So, in this case, we find ourselves in the midst of a lot of trouble at present because, without it, we cannot grow. It seems to me, Mr. President, it is God's will for us to suffer as we are presently doing. Jesus, in Gethsemane, asked the Father to take the cup from him, if it was the Father's will. But the Father asked Jesus to accept being nailed to the cross. If we will not accept the pain and suffering and misunderstanding of this moment, how can we even think of pleasing God or doing his will?"

The president didn't speak. His displeasure was evident to all his aides.

The meeting was terminated without any conclusions having been reached for a positive line of action.

In Detroit, the next day, an ugly crowd gathered to hear Samuel Joseph deliver a major campaign address. At one point he was drowned out by their singing "Rock of Ages." Crucifixes were plainly visible throughout the hall. A militant lady from Dearborn, carrying a gun, stood up and shouted at him, "Do you accept Jesus Christ as your personal lord and savior?" Immediately, fistfights broke out. The police stormed the hall. No one could say precisely what happened next. Mass pandemonium ensued and then, without warning, all the lights went out.

The 26 dead and 690 injured persons provided a

desperately sobering statistic to a divided nation.

The president, appearing on television, looked more drawn and harried than the public had ever seen him before. He had engaged in an all-night meeting with Ron Dixon and other aides.

"The forms of divisiveness must be overwhelmingly repudiated," he told the nation. "America is founded on principles of religious toleration, social justice, and human compassion. Religion must be a unifying force, not a destructive one. Men's approaches to God must heal old wounds, not inflict new ones. I call upon the American people, in this tragic hour, to pray for peace in the stead of conflict, for brotherhood in the place of strife, and for national unity of many brothers under one God."

Reaction to the president's speech was violent. Fifteen thousand hymn-singing protesters, carrying guns, marched angrily on the White House. The mob's head-on confrontation with the National Guard was bloody.

That night, Philip Anderson spoke in San Francisco. The invocation opening the meeting was given by Ellsworth Pinkney. Bruce Whippick led the 30,000 assembled people in singing "What a Friend We Have in Jesus."

At first, the crowd did not sense what was happening. Gripped in the frenzy of religious fervor, their bodies swaying and close together, the people remained unaware of the building rhythm of a movement undergirding their own. The ground rolled beneath them, seeming to move in concert with their pitched cries and muscular thrusts.

When the earthquake sustained its five-minute uninterrupted peak, as the West Coast of the United States split asunder, the crowd disappeared, screaming and writhing, into the belly of the earth. The ensuing tidal wave swallowed it up.

The nation was caught in the greatest catastrophe and emergency in its history. Raging waters swept inland, submerging San Diego, Los Angeles, San Francisco, Portland, and Seattle. Movie stars were now rarer than imperial gems. Cable cars had vanished from the face of the continent.

Led by the president, the country embarked upon a period of penitence and self-examination. The president himself endorsed Samuel Joseph, who was elected the first Jewish chief executive by receiving 97 per cent of the vote.

Pulpits were strangely silent when it came to offering theological interpretations of the disaster. The Ellsworth Pinkney Foundation for

Judeo-Christian Dialogues was opened in Washington, D.C. A new song, "Jesus, Jewish Boy and Jewish Man," became an overnight American classic, in both a religious and a secular sense.

Within one year, there were more Jews in America than Baptists, Methodists, and Catholics combined.

3

Odor
of Espresso

Father Art had decided years ago to be avant-garde but it had been necessary for him to repress his feelings. In the first place, he was an Irish priest and nobody expected him to have a vast, hidden life which cut against his outward actions. His image seemed all of a piece and secure.

As a curate and later the pastor of a sprawling, successful Bingo parish in a big city, he had been dutifully jovial, telling his Irish Catholic stories, attending ball games with the kids, preaching safe and patriotic sermons, and standing like a rock for mariology, masses, and motherhood.

He had been jolted out of his wits when he was assigned to St. Cyprian's where his superiors felt he could do more good ministering to the very rich. At first he had been defensive and careful,

always being conscious of his own background of
poverty and earthiness. But then he had begun
smelling the possibilities. He could now come out
of his secret shell and be as avant-garde as he had
wished in forbidden and old fantasies.

Rolling Hills was one of the most distinguished
and rich suburbs in America. St. Cyprian's was a
gem. It had cost a million dollars and could hold
only two hundred people. The eucharistic vest-
ments were medieval French and the chalice had a
star sapphire in it.

It was a tight, happy Christian family at St.
Cyprian's. Social climbers in the holy of holies
were few and soon learned that though they could
have communion, they would choke on it later
when no one spoke to them or apparently even
saw their brightly eager middle-class faces.

Father Art could hold his gin, learned to spot
the differences in vintage wines, and won the confidence not only of his parishioners but also of the
Rolling Hills community. "Father Art's a nice
guy" was the consensus. Actually, Father Art
developed an ulcer as he stepped lightly among
his flock, never rocking the boat nor stirring deep
waters. For the past several years he had wanted
to stand for something other than equanimity, but
there seemed to be no issues in Rolling Hills—or,

to put it more precisely, the only issues he could find wouldn't permit him to take a stand on them. If he had opened his mouth, he would have been sent packing by nightfall. He didn't see what good he could accomplish in Rolling Hills if he were sent precipitously into exile, so he kept silent (except for preaching the gospel on Sunday mornings, of course) and stayed on.

He baptized babies extraordinarily well. They never cried, the story went, even when he was slopping their heads with cold water. He married people beautifully, thereby joining grace to the highest social prestige. His burials moved observers to tears, quite aside from whom the deceased might happen to be. It was partly due to his deep, ringing voice and his spectacularly clean-cut, sincere, handsome appearance. Yet, if he had lacked these, Father Art would still have possessed his magical quality, his "style." It set him apart from other men whether he was at a cocktail party or the altar, in the Country Club or the pulpit.

Father Art was, simply, a resounding success. Pledging was up to inflationary levels in the parish, a new half-million-dollar educational building was about to begin construction, and word was honeycombing the eastern establishment that a new Bishop was being made. A shrewd religious publishing house had, in fact, recently asked Father Art to write a book, to be entitled modestly, *Memoirs and Chasubles: The Early Years.*

Yet Father Art began to feel as if he were suffocated in St. Cyprian's. He longed for the moment when he might openly express his avantgarde feelings. Noting that students were simply disinterested in the church, he wanted to bring them back, and arouse their sleeping parents, by sharply relevant developments. The church must be revolutionary, he felt, but how to bring this about in Rolling Hills escaped him.

At that moment in Father Art's life, Agnes DuLuth came back to Rolling Hills. The DuLuths were unquestionably the leading family. They had made about a billion dollars in railroads, ships, planes, copper, steel, and tires. Agnes was their only child. She had been a debutante, and, after graduating from Radcliffe, went off to Paris. She dabbled in existentialism, bought paintings, wrote poetry, and married a Portuguese revolutionary-in-exile. In Paris and later in Rolling Hills, he was known as Juan.

. Agnes and Juan met Father Art at a party which the DuLuths gave for the French consul.

"We're back to settle down," Agnes told

Father Art. "Europe was absolutely thrilling but one can't just keep running all the time."

"We plan to carve out a life for ourselves, if I might put it that way, back here in Rolling Hills, Father," Juan said.

"You can help me," Father Art told them. After that night he was in touch with them every day. They would have lunch or talk endlessly over the phone, meet for a drink or make plans over dinner.

"We're not going to belong to church," Agnes told him, "but we want to help you. Is that all right? It's just too late for us to get mixed up in church things again but being mixed up with you will be amusing and terribly stimulating."

Through their eyes, Father Art saw the world in a startlingly new light. He felt that he must be involved in *it* rather than merely in church matters. Agnes and Juan took him to concerts, art shows, the theater, the best foreign films and lectures. Where there had previously been an obstructive wall within his life, now there was an altogether new dimension of freedom and discovery.

"It's time for change in Rolling Hills," Juan remarked one night after the three of them had been to a concert.

"That's the way I feel," Father Art said. "I want the church to lead the way. But first the church has to be changed from merely an expensive and prestigious private club."

"I don't agree," Agnes replied. "The church can only be changed itself as it becomes a part of the entire process of change in the community."

Agnes and Juan felt that Rolling Hills must become culturally activated. An emphasis on art, music, and drama should replace the round of parties, life at the Country Club, and in-fighting gossip. All the power alignments in the community were terrified because Agnes could pull them apart as putty in her hands. She decided to do battle for her cause and got underway by throwing her own collection of modern art into the balance of power. It was one of the important collections in the country.

Wanting to make the church dramatically contemporary, Father Art asked Agnes if he might show the collection for the first time publicly in St. Cyprian's. It would be on a Sunday morning during regular worship services. Juan was amused, but Agnes took the invitation with deep seriousness and agreed.

A total cultural assault was Father Art's plan.

The medium would be the gospel in an unprecedented way. On the first Sunday in Advent, when
Rolling Hills society walked into St. Cyprian's for
divine worship, it experienced a head-on collision
with the world of art. The night before, moving
vans had transported Agnes' collection of modern
art to the church. Abstract designs were at eye-
level with steel executives. A jazz combo, imported from an avant-garde downtown hot spot,
struck up the processional hymn. The president of
the Junior League did an interpretive dance, accompanied by an Indian student playing the sitar,
for the offertory. Instead of the sermon, the Rolling Hills New Ideas Theatre presented a reading
of the story of Jerry and the Dog from *The Zoo
Story* as a sanctuary drama. High school students
dressed in clown costumes acted as ushers, wearing buttons reading: "All the World's a Stage:
Are *You* Playing *Your* Part?"

Rolling Hills decided, quite spontaneously and
without collusion, not to become disturbed. The
immediate reaction, therefore, took the form of no
reaction. At the church door when he greeted parishioners leaving St. Cyprian's after the service,
Father Art met only pleasant smiles and plati-
tudes. "Wasn't the choir marvelous today?" "It

∾

was a wonderful sermon." "We enjoyed it." Back
in their homes, people did not discuss church that
Sunday.

Agnes and Juan wrote off the church and pur-
sued their cultural program with renewed zeal and
new approaches. For them, success was a fore-
gone conclusion. Father Art realized, however,
that he was faced with a terrible problem. He
could give up and accommodate the people of St.
Cyprian's in their clear desire to be left alone, or
he could persist against great odds in his desire to
make St. Cyprian's relevant and revolutionary.
He chose the latter course. Yet how could Rolling
Hills be *reached?* He wanted a clear response
from the community, even if it must be anger. If
the art world could not deeply stir Rolling Hills,
then he must turn to social issues.

Poverty was, of course, not an issue understood
in Rolling Hills. War seemed remote—one observed it on TV while drinking Beefeater-on-the-
rocks. Anti-Semitism was not a problem because
there were no Jews.

One met Jews downtown in the bustling arena
of finance, and at great civic luncheons related to
brotherhood, but the community itself remained
gentile as well as white. There *was* an exception to
its whiteness: the young scion of a leading family,

related to the DuLuths, had married an Oriental princess. This was always mentioned as an example of the community's complete openness and liberalism when the racial question was raised. Many blacks worked in Rolling Hills as butlers, maids, chauffeurs, and cooks. Lunching at the club (known affectionately as the Big Club), the community's matrons deplored violence in the streets. They were certain black militancy was directly attributable to communist infiltration. After all, they "knew their Negroes," who had solemnly assured them of their opposition to black power and "uppity niggers."

Rolling Hills remembered the brief shadow which civil rights had, in the mid-sixties, cast over the community. A young Presbyterian assistant minister had, in fact, in a hysterical and frenzied moment opted to march in Selma. Upon his return he was quietly and immediately disposed of. Father Art vaguely recalled that he either became a missionary in the Philippines or else took a church in southwest Montana. But the young Presbyterian's emotional action was the only example of religious frenzy within the area's recorded history.

It was clearly time, Father Art decided, to have more religious frenzy in Rolling Hills. This could serve to jolt people into existential involvement. After all, the apostolic early church had been in and out of jails, was led by social undesirables, and spreckled with civil disobedience, political malcontents, and violence.

Father Art spent more and more time away from Rolling Hills. He made contacts within the inner-city of the adjoining metropolis, in relation to which Rolling Hills was a mythical and royal suburb. He had decided that St. Cyprian's must be forced into a confrontation with social issues. He gave priority to black power. Now he was looking within the inner-city for just one thing: black nationalists. He felt he must become informed at firsthand if he were to be the moral leader which his ordination as a priest seemed to signify.

His search was slow and painstaking. He established the essential beachhead of his operation when, at an inner-city art museum evening seminar on African sculpture, he met a young, very black man who looked angry and refused to engage in the social amenities of politeness or mere forms, such as shaking hands when introduced to whites. The young man's name was Henry Brown. Father Art knew immediately that Brown represented his breakthrough. He was amazed to dis-

cover that Brown was the son of a maid, Thelma
Brown, who worked in a Rolling Hills home.

Henry Brown, while opposed to white involvement in the black revolution, was intrigued by
Father Art's strange naïveté and earnest resolve
for St. Cyprian's. He came to agree with Father
Art that the strategy of confronting St. Cyprian's
with black power could be mutually beneficial. It
would assist Father Art to do *his* job, as a white
man working in the white community, to awaken
whites to political and social reality. It could
represent an unusual opportunity to make the
white power structure aware of black power in an
intensely direct way.

Within a short time, Father Art was catapulted
into a whole new world of ghetto blackness. He ate
soul food. He heard soul music. Regarded with
suspicion, he was partly accepted as a friend of
Henry Brown. Seesawing between the two worlds,
one in Rolling Hills and another in the black
ghetto, he sometimes felt as if he were losing all
sense of his own identity. One evening he was
present at a dinner party in the Big Club, the next
he was engaged in a new kind of naked dialogue
with angry young revolutionaries. He could not
see bridging the separate worlds but simply felt

he must make St. Cyprian's aware of their existence.

Father Art embarrassed Henry Brown's mother by seeking her out in the home where she worked.

"Mrs. Brown, I know your son Henry and I promised him I'd come to see you."

"Thank you, Father."

"He seems to be getting along well. He's taking courses in night school at the university and has a job. I guess you know this."

"I'm glad. Yes, I talked to his sister last week and heard about him. I'm certainly glad."

"Can I give him a message from you, Mrs. Brown?"

"Why, I can't think of anything in particular, Father. Just tell him I'm certainly glad he's fine and getting along well."

"All right, Mrs. Brown, I'll do that."

She had never changed her expression or voice, but he knew she didn't like his intrusion into her life. Henry Brown continued to help him make plans for an assault on St. Cyprian's conscience.

One night he met Henry Brown late in a bar near the university where he took night courses. The juke box was loud as they drank beer and talked.

"White priest, what in hell are you doing in

here?'' a young black man, suddenly at his elbow, asked Father Art.

"It's okay, Archie, he's my friend," said Brown. "He's with me."

"I don't care, man, who he's with. I just want Whitey to answer my question. Whitey, white priest, what in hell are you doing in here?''

"I'm with my friend, Henry Brown, and I'm drinking a beer and talking," Father Art replied.

"You come in here to save me, white priest? *You* come in here to save *me* with your white God and your white Jesus, Whitey?''

"No. I'm just with my friend, Henry Brown."

"This is a black man's hole. Can't you even leave a black man his own hole, Whitey?''

"I'm sorry. This is Henry Brown and I'm just drinking a beer with him and talking."

"White priest, I'm for *black* religion. My God is black, man. My God isn't your God, man.''

After this, Father Art felt more strongly than ever that time was running out. The people of Rolling Hills who attended St. Cyprian's must be told about life outside their rich, white ghetto. As a matter of fact, Father Art got to know Archie, who helped Henry Brown make the plans for St. Cyprian's which were in motion.

Father Art did not give Rolling Hills even a

slight warning as to what would shortly transpire. Lent was now drawing to a close, with Easter just around the corner. The time seemed propitious. Perhaps Easter could indeed mean resurrection, renewal, and new life this year for the parish and community.

Good Friday went quietly. There was the traditional observance of the afternoon three-hour service. This was, as always, solidly attended by the women of Rolling Hills. It had, over the years, become a very "in" thing. On Easter Eve, Father Art baptized a dozen babies in the church. The community found this as inspiring as always. Late afternoon shadows filled the gemlike church, deepening its always intrinsic drama. Candlelight flickered against Father Art's handsome, clean face as he sprinkled water on the babies' bright young faces and baptized them in the name of the Trinity. A grande-dame godmother was moved to gentle tears by the spectacle. Afterward, there were cocktails at the Big Club. Then Rolling Hills slowly unwound. Tomorrow would be the High Day of the social year—Easter at St. Cyprian's.

It was almost like rolling away the huge stone from the empty tomb as the first parishioners opened the heavy bronze door of St. Cyprian's the

next morning. They wanted to flee but stood trans-
fixed, gazing at the life-size jet black figure of
Jesus, garbed in a black loincloth, hanging over
the altar.

A black choir, bused from the inner-city, sang
the processional hymn "Swing Low, Sweet
Chariot." The church bulletin contained the announcement that, on Tuesday evenings at 8:30,
there would be a fifteen-session course on Afro-
American History and Culture, conducted by a
well-known black militant who was a social
worker in a settlement house. The Easter sermon
was preached by a militant black preacher and
freedom fighter, a Baptist, who had been flown to
Rolling Hills from Birmingham, Alabama.

The Easter collection, it was explained in the
bulletin, would not go to the building fund for the
new educational building but instead would be
given to the Negro College Fund. Sunday School
classes were dispensed with, and the youth of St.
Cyprian's heard an address by a young black
nationalist out on bail following a recent civil
disorder in the city.

Paintings by black artists filled the sanctuary.
A performance in Rolling Hills of Genet's *The
Blacks,* as a sanctuary drama in St. Cyprian's to

be performed by Afro-American actors from an inner-city coffeehouse theater, was announced for the following weekend.

Rolling Hills responded with *noblesse oblige*. The preacher, before catching a plane back to Alabama, was feted at a dinner party in the Big Club. The series of classes on Afro-American History and Culture was immediately oversubscribed. The offering hit a new high level. The young militant who addressed the Sunday School was enthusiastically asked to return in order to speak at a high school assembly. Tickets to *The Blacks* were unobtainable within three days. The Altar Guild wondered if a picture of the new *Christus* over the altar might not appear on the next year's church calendar.

Shortly thereafter, a black millionaire wished to buy a home for his family in Rolling Hills. His son attended graduate school at Harvard, his daughter was a sophomore at Sarah Lawrence, and he was a principal benefactor of the symphony. His request was granted and the new family moved into the community. Rolling Hills now felt more liberal than it had even when the local scion married the Oriental princess.

Father Art, outwardly poised, was a churning

mad charade inside himself. Henry Brown had
been more than satisfied with the success of black
power's confrontation with St. Cyprian's, and
was back in the city's ghetto. Unruffled by events,
St. Cyprian's was unchanged except that it felt
somewhat more self-righteous than before. It
knew now that its capacity for resistance to
change was a mastered art.

Continuing to spend time outside Rolling Hills,
Father Art tried to keep very close to changing
political and social currents of thought. He had
established contact with students at the great inner-city university and a state university not far
away. He refused to relax his efforts to awaken
St. Cyprian's to revolutionary change. The peace
movement was of major importance to students,
Father Art knew, and he thought he might somehow be able to make St. Cyprian's deeply sensi-
tive to it.

He announced a week's fast in the interests of
world peace, with prayers for a cessation of fight-
ing. It began with an all-night vigil in the church.
The crowd exceeded Easter's in size. Everybody
fasted. One matron lost eight pounds and canceled
her scheduled semi-annual visit to Elizabeth
Arden's Main Chance. Several parishioners commented that this beat giving up liquor for Lent.

As a concentrated "crash" diet it worked, and spiritually one felt one had *done* something.

Feeling the ground give way beneath him, Father Art decided he must summon final resources of strength in order to awaken the community to authentic involvement. His weapons would be his new, deepening contacts within the student world. Already youth comprised approximately half the national population. If youth could not be interested in Christianity in an honest and compelling way, then the church would probably not even be alive in fifty years.

Father Art came to grips with his new apostolate. He shared his problems at St. Cyprian's with new friends among students at the two universities. They offered to help him. After visiting the church, and quietly meeting some of the parishioners, they offered Father Art their idea. He should, they said, open a coffeehouse in the basement of St. Cyprian's. It would provide a touch of authentic scandal to needle people into expressing their true feelings. Then Father Art could, for the first time, engage them as human beings in honest controversy. They would no longer be role playing on their own terms of status quo and polite dismissal of real issues.

No one in the church opposed the idea of the

coffeehouse. Students painted the walls in a combination of religious and secular motifs. An espresso machine sent from Italy was on hand for the lively opening. The coffeehouse was called "The Appian Way." Immediately it became very chic and was featured on the society page of the city's leading newspaper. On the opening night, underground films were shown and a young Cuban poet recited revolutionary verse. Parents were delighted with the project. A virtual Social Register of women signed up to make coffee, wash cups and saucers, and mop the floor in shifts.

The students were as appalled as Father Art. Rolling Hills had no mortal flesh to needle, no conscience to be stirred. Father Art was taking steps to seek a transfer when, overnight, the picture changed. Unplanned, genuine controversy finally came to St. Cyprian's.

A student in "The Appian Way" was arrested by a police officer for smoking pot. Most students insisted that the police officer planted marijuana on the young man. Whatever the facts might be, veritable emotional maelstorm ensued. Debate raged within family circles, the Big Club was split right down the middle on the issue (the arrested student was related to a leading family), there were cries alike of "moral decency" and "police brutality," and "The Appian Way" was photographed by *Time, Newsweek,* and *Life.* Rolling Hills was outraged, considering publicity the only essential vulgarity.

Clergy in every part of America gave sermons alluding to "moral degeneracy" as found in a church-related coffeehouse which seemed to be a dope den. A former child actress in California, now a respectable matron, declared she would not drink another cup of coffee until "the dirty coffeehouse in the underground church" had been closed and padlocked. The White House made an indirect but immediately identifiable reference to the incident in the course of remarks at a presidential prayer breakfast.

Father Art gathered with some students to discuss the incident and determine future action.

"That church bag doesn't seem right for you, Father," one student said. "They're all hypocrites and it's hopeless. Why don't you get out and try to land a job with the Peace Corps or a poverty program?"

"I'm not questioning at all what you're saying," Father Art replied. "But I believe in the church beneath the church. Under the organization, you see, and all the forms, is a reality for me. I think my place is to stay."

"But you can't stay, can you?" another student asked. "They seem to want your hide, Father. I mean, you keep trying to wake them up and they'll bomb you before they let you really get to them in a nitty-gritty sense."

"Well, I didn't take this church for popularity," Father Art said. "Being a priest isn't being a worldly success. I'm not a masochist but I think I've got to stand my ground."

"You're a nice guy, Father, but I'm sure through with the church after this," another student said. "Pardon me, but I'm fed up. I want to get away from double-standard morality and I feel the church lives that way. You're okay up to now, but so what does that mean? It doesn't change the institution."

Flower children, Ivy League students with pot, and some hardened addicts began arriving in Rolling Hills. Since there was no hotel, they slept in the completed basement of St. Cyprian's new educational building. Rumors about sex orgies spread quickly.

Publicity mounted. *The Wall Street Journal* ran a front-page depth report on the developing affair. TV camera crews from New York interviewed matrons outside the Big Club. (They were barred from setting foot inside it.) *Holiday* can-

celed a story about Rolling Hills pending the out-
come of events.

Father Art hadn't had a real talk with Agnes
DuLuth and Juan for a long time. He called them
and they invited him to dinner.

"We feel guilty we haven't seen you," Agnes
said. "My God, what are they doing to you?"

"What are you going to do?" asked Juan.

"I suppose just stay until I'm kicked out or this
blows over," Father Art told them.

"It's absolutely incredible," Agnes responded.
"I feel so sorry for you. No. Don't tell me not to
say that. I don't mean to be demeaning. I'm not
patronizing. I'm just so sorry for you, not as a
priest but as a man. Can we do anything to help?"

"We'd like to help if we can," Juan interjected.
"This is really all so ridiculous. You're trapped
in a lot of nonsense. You can't let yourself be
destroyed."

"I appreciate your friendship," Father Art
told them. "I don't think you can help in any
other way right now but just to let me talk and
know friends are listening."

A few days later, Father Art made his tragic
and irremediable move. He grew a beard.

No one ever knew precisely why he did. Young

Archie and Henry Brown and other black nationalists grew beards, and it was known that Father
Art admired them. A number of university students whom he knew also grew beards. But no
clear line of connection between anyone else's
beard and his was ever drawn.

However, his growing a beard caused communication to break down at every level within the
community. Some saw him as a saint, even a
modern Jesus-figure, while others flatly claimed
he was a communist or a fanatic. When a guru
representing Eastern mysticism flew from India
to visit the now world-famous coffeehouse, and
was photographed with Father Art, all hell simply broke loose. The Big Club closed "for altera-
tions," but, in fact, it was dangerous to congre-
gate in Rolling Hills, and best friends had ceased
speaking to one another.

As Father Art's beard grew bushier and
heavier, so attendance at St. Cyprian's diminished in alarming proportions.

There has been endless speculation about the
last night. It is a known fact that Henry Brown
and some five other black nationalists met with
Father Art in the rectory for approximately one
hour. It is also documented that Agnes and Juan

were with him for forty minutes. Two or more students from the inner-city university dropped in for a chat with him shortly after ten o'clock.

After that, nothing is known. The next morning, he was gone. Father Art seemingly vanished from the face of the earth. Rumors have placed him everywhere. One school of thought claimed he had been murdered, and his body cremated in the basement of the Big Club. A Chicago *Sun-Times* dispatch circulated the report he was a guru in Nepal. A religion writer for the St. Louis *Post-Dispatch* suspected his presence among Latin American revolutionaries, while the Cleveland *Plain-Dealer* hinted he was active as a guerrilla priest in the U.S. urban underground. From London came reports that he had joined a celebrated singing group to open a clandestine meditation center in Tonga.

To the horror of the parishioners, St. Cyprian's was never able to lock its doors again, at any hour of the day or night. Thousands of people flocked there to meditate, with the number increasing each year.

Father Preston-Armistead, who followed Father Art at St. Cyprian's, was a gray, conciliatory figure. The parish flourished economically, but the spark had gone. Of course, "The Appian Way" was discontinued. In fact, the basement of St. Cyprian's, following a short but respectable period of disuse, was turned over to the Altar Guild for its meetings. There was an unwritten law, preserved by oral tradition, that coffee was strictly banned. Inside the site of the former coffeehouse, only tea could now be served.

Despite repeated scrubbing and fumigation, and outcries of indignation from the ladies, the odor of espresso coffee clung resolutely to that hallowed room. Lately, rumors have circulated wildly in Rolling Hills that the curious odor grows stronger and stronger with each passing year.

[4]

A Study
in Color

A THEATRICAL SKETCH

[Two persons are seated on a bare stage. One rather harsh, bright spot shines on one of the persons, a similar spot on the other. One person is seated on a severely straightback chair, the other on a high stool. Each is isolated from the other person, oblivious of his presence on the stage. A white actor wears black trousers, black socks, black shoes, a black shirt, and a black mask with Caucasian features (he is reading Ebony*), while a black actor wears white trousers, white socks, white shoes, a white shirt, and a white mask with Negroid features (he is reading* Town and Country*).]*

BLACK WEARING WHITE MASK: I become so bored with color. [*Pause*] As a matter of fact, I wish I

❧

had some. [*Self-consciously stretches and yawns.*]
All of this race jazz. [*Picks up a magazine, leafs
through it for a moment, is bored and somewhat
preoccupied and puts it down; speaks now with
more earnestness, as if trying to say something,
to make some point.*] I mean, what *is* color? Well,
you know, on a human being. Is it like being a
painting, is it something like being a painting all
the time, you know, walking around like a painting
among a lot of non-paintings. What is a non-painting? [*Shrugs*] It's so complex, it's hard to talk
about intelligibly. I'm sorry, I know there isn't
such a thing as a non-painting, but . . . [*Pause*]
I become so bored, so bored. With being just white.
I want some *color,* I want some *color.* Actually,
they say most of the world will be colored. [*Pause*]
Color is so beautiful, isn't it? Blue. Yellow. Red.
And I'm just white all the time. Washed out. Pale.
Pallid. Antiseptically clean. Dull, it's so damned
boring. [*Picks up the magazine again and starts
reading it.*]

WHITE WEARING BLACK MASK: I wish that just one
white man could understand . . . just once . . .
how a Negro *feels,* what goes through a Negro's
mind. A white man is stupid when it comes to
Negroes. [*Pause*] Like the white woman who has

just put up a "for sale" sign in her yard, and she
happens to run into the Negro woman who has
moved in next door, and she tells her, my dear,
you know, my husband has a *heart* condition, and
we're going to have to move . . . right away . . .
because we've got to move from this two-story
house into a one-story house . . . immediately
. . . in another part of town . . . [*Pause*] Man.

BLACK WEARING WHITE MASK: [*Tosses the magazine onto the floor.*] Nigger. [*Long pause; he is
reflecting upon this word.*] Nigger. [*Then, with
great deliberation and care*] Negro. [*Pause*] I wonder what it's like to be a Negro. What it's like to
be a Nigger. Would I be different. Would I *feel*
different? [*Pause*] I feel so black and blue, I feel
so black and white, I feel so black. [*Pause, lights
a cigarette*] Black ivory, black velvet, black cloud,
black eyes, black night, black sin. Black face. Black
arms. Black chest. Black feet. Red lips. Brown
lips. Black hair. White teeth.

WHITE WEARING BLACK MASK: You know, I *dislike*
the name Nigger. I dislike the name Nigger.
[*Pause*] Cleanse my sins and I shall be whiter
than white. Wash me in the blood of the lamb, and
I shall be *white*, wash me in the blood of the lamb,

and I shall be *white*. [*Pause*] My blackness is hot,
my blackness is hot, send a white angel so I can be
cool under its wings, cool under its white cool
wings.

BLACK WEARING WHITE MASK: [*He is telling a joke.*]
They were all waiting at the Washington airport
for God to arrive in a space ship. They were all
waiting to see what God looked like. And then God
got off the space ship, and God, *she* was *Negro*.
[*Laughs, almost gets out of control, is utterly car-
ried away with the humor of this.*] *She* was *Negro*.
God was a *Nigger*. [*Gradually regains control of
himself; then sits and thinks for a moment.*] My
God is a Nigger. I am a Nigger lover because I
love my God. Jesus Christ. Nigger Christ. Christ
Nigger. [*Pause*]

WHITE WEARING BLACK MASK: Coal white. Tar
white, dirty white, white white, ugly white. White
ivory, white velvet, white cloud, white eyes.
[*Laughs*] White night [*Finds this very funny.*]
White sin. Oh, my God. [*Pause*] White face.
White hair. White teeth. *Black* teeth. [*Finds this
very, very, funny, breaks up completely.*] Black
teeth, black teeth. Black *teeth, black* teeth.
[*Gradually regains composure, then sits quietly.*]
BLACK WEARING WHITE MASK: I know what I'm

∾

going to do. I'm going to experiment with color.
Experiment: [*He opens a small briefcase and
takes out a mask which is painted with polkadots;
he examines it, holding it in his hands.*] This is
pretty, I think. I'm bored with white and this is
red and yellow and green and blue and black and
purple. I think I'll wear it. I think I'll wear a
mask. Why not? I'm not really being dishonest,
I'm still me, I'll still be me, but it will be a change.
I wonder what my friends will say, I wonder if
they'll know me? But I'll still be me, won't I, I'll
still be *me.* [*Places the mask over his face and
remains seated.*]

WHITE WEARING BLACK MASK: I am a *colored* man.
[*Picks up a book and reads it for a few minutes,
then puts it down.*] If I'm supposed to be *colored,*
then I'm going to be colored. [*He opens a small
briefcase and takes out a mask which is brightly
painted with stripes; he examines it, holding it in
his hands; then he places it over his face.*]

[*An overhead light comes on replacing the two
single spots. The two persons become conscious of
each other for the first time.*]

BLACK WEARING POLKADOT MASK OVER WHITE MASK:
Hello.

WHITE WEARING STRIPED MASK OVER BLACK MASK:
Hi.

BLACK WEARING POLKADOT MASK OVER WHITE MASK:
It's a nice day, isn't it?

WHITE WEARING STRIPED MASK OVER BLACK MASK:
Well, if you call it a nice day when it's raining,
then, sure, it's a nice day.

BLACK WEARING POLKADOT MASK OVER WHITE MASK:
I'm only trying to . . . make a conversation.

WHITE WEARING STRIPED MASK OVER BLACK MASK:
Why are you trying to do that?

BLACK WEARING POLKADOT MASK OVER WHITE MASK:
If you feel that way about it, then I won't try.

WHITE WEARING STRIPED MASK OVER BLACK MASK:
That's okay by me. [*They sit in silence.*] Hell, I'm
sorry. I'm just in a bad mood today. There's no
use not *talking*. Here. Have a cigarette?

BLACK WEARING POLKADOT MASK OVER WHITE MASK:
Is it a filter? I only smoke filters.

A STUDY
IN COLOR

WHITE WEARING STRIPED MASK OVER BLACK MASK:
No. It's not a filter.

BLACK WEARING POLKADOT MASK OVER WHITE MASK:
Then I'll smoke my own. Thanks. Thanks for
offering me one. But I get a sore throat when I
don't smoke a filter. You know?

WHITE WEARING STRIPED MASK OVER BLACK MASK:
[*Pause*] It's stopped raining.

BLACK WEARING POLKADOT MASK OVER WHITE MASK:
The weather bureau didn't say it would rain any-
way. [*They sit in silence.*] I hope you don't mind
my saying this, I hope you're not, well, self-con-
scious about this, but . . . well, you know, this is
the first time I've really *talked* with a colored
man.

WHITE WEARING STRIPED MASK OVER BLACK MASK:
What?

BLACK WEARING POLKADOT MASK OVER WHITE MASK:
I hope you're not offended, I didn't mean to offend
you, but it's true, it's the first time I've really,
well, *talked,* you know, with a colored man.

WHITE WEARING STRIPED MASK OVER BLACK MASK:
Well, actually . . .

BLACK WEARING POLKADOT MASK OVER WHITE MASK:
I've wondered what it's like, what it must be like,
to be colored. You know, in a white society. I hate
all this prejudice. The root of prejudice surely is
ignorance. I think the answer to everything is
more education. [*Pause*] God, I hate the South.

WHITE WEARING STRIPED MASK OVER BLACK MASK:
The South?

BLACK WEARING POLKADOT MASK OVER WHITE MASK:
Yes, all that race prejudice. All the discrimina-
tion. The race hate. Some of my best friends are
southern whites but . . .

WHITE WEARING STRIPED MASK OVER BLACK MASK:
You're . . . you're a northern *white?*

BLACK WEARING POLKADOT MASK OVER WHITE MASK:
No. I'm a western white. I just happen to be living
in the North.

WHITE WEARING STRIPED MASK OVER BLACK MASK:
But . . . you're *white?*

❧

BLACK WEARING POLKADOT MASK OVER WHITE MASK:
White? Why, of course I'm a white. What made
you ask a thing like that? Oh! This *mask*. [*Laughs*]
Well, I was experimenting. Experimenting with
color.

WHITE WEARING STRIPED MASK OVER BLACK MASK:
You do have some beautiful colors.

BLACK WEARING POLKADOT MASK OVER WHITE MASK:
May I say that you are yourself one of the most,
well, *attractive* colored persons I've ever seen? It
embarrasses me a bit, even makes me angry, when
I realize that I have all the advantages of being
white, and I just wear this mask when I *want* to,
but you're *colored,* you're colored all the time, you
can't take a mask off or put it on when you want
to. It makes me really angry.

WHITE WEARING STRIPED MASK OVER BLACK MASK:
Why?

BLACK WEARING POLKADOT MASK OVER WHITE MASK:
It's . . . it's so unjust.

WHITE WEARING STRIPED MASK OVER BLACK MASK:
I'm not colored. I'm black. [*Abruptly removes
striped mask.*]

∾

BLACK WEARING POLKADOT MASK OVER WHITE MASK:
Oh. [*Long pause; then slowly removes his polka-dot mask.*] I . . . I don't know what to say.
[*Long pause*] I thought you were colored and you're not colored, you're black. You're only black. [*Long pause*] You had . . . such *nice* colors. I liked them.

WHITE WEARING BLACK MASK: Don't you like my black?

BLACK WEARING WHITE MASK: I didn't say I don't like your black, I just said I liked your . . . colors. Why are you so touchy? Why are you so touchy about being black?

WHITE WEARING BLACK MASK: Who said I'm touchy about being black?

BLACK WEARING WHITE MASK: I don't know, you just . . . seem to be touchy about . . . being black, that's all. [*Long pause*] Why did you wear a *colored* mask? Why didn't you wear a *white* mask? I'm sure you could find one.

WHITE WEARING BLACK MASK: Why should I wear a white mask?

BLACK WEARING WHITE MASK: Oh, I don't know. It's . . . a white culture, after all, and it's easier being a . . . white man.

WHITE WEARING BLACK MASK: Is it?

BLACK WEARING WHITE MASK: God, you're so touchy. You're so touchy. [Long pause] Well, since you don't *want* to be friends . . .

WHITE WEARING BLACK MASK: I didn't say I don't want to be friends.

BLACK WEARING WHITE MASK: [Heated, angry] You're so darned conscious of being a nigger . . . [abrupt pause] of being black . . . [pause] . . . that you go around with all kinds of misconceptions about how other people *feel* . . . you . . . you *judge* everybody . . . just because some people are ignorant or prejudiced, you feel that . . . that . . . everybody . . . [Long pause]

WHITE WEARING BLACK MASK: Look. I'm sorry. If I offended you or seemed to be rude, I'm sorry.

BLACK WEARING WHITE MASK: [Pause] I am, too. I don't know what's the trouble with me. It's just a

bad day, I guess. [*Pause*] Would you mind . . .
I have an idea, there's something I'd like to do but
I don't know how you'll feel about it and . . .

WHITE WEARING BLACK MASK: What is it? Tell me.

BLACK WEARING WHITE MASK: Would you mind . . .
if we exchanged roles, exchanged masks, for just
a few minutes?

WHITE WEARING BLACK MASK: [*Pause*] No. That's
okay by me. [*Each removes his mask.*]

BLACK WHO HAS BEEN WEARING WHITE MASK: You're
so *black*. You're such a *dark* Negro. [*The white
player who has been playing the black now puts on
the white mask, and the black player who has been
playing the white now puts on the black mask.
There ensues a primitive ritual marked by casual
dance movement and the playing of bongos.*]

WHITE WEARING WHITE MASK: Hi.

BLACK WEARING BLACK MASK: Hello.

WHITE WEARING WHITE MASK: I'm white. Are you
black?

BLACK WEARING BLACK MASK: What difference does it make?

WHITE WEARING WHITE MASK: I just wondered.

BLACK WEARING BLACK MASK: Does it make any difference?

WHITE WEARING WHITE MASK: I suppose not. [*Pause*] Well, statistically, they want to know.

BLACK WEARING BLACK MASK: Know *what?*

WHITE WEARING WHITE MASK: Know who's white and who's black.

BLACK WEARING BLACK MASK: Why?

WHITE WEARING WHITE MASK: I don't know. They just want to *know*.

BLACK WEARING BLACK MASK: Who are they?

WHITE WEARING WHITE MASK: I don't know. They just want to know. [*Pause*] Well, I'm white.

BLACK WEARING BLACK MASK: Are you?

❦

WHITE WEARING WHITE MASK: [*Defensively.*] Yes, yes, I am . . . [*Changes mood.*] But to tell you the truth, I can't really tell whether you're black or, well, just . . . tanned. I'm really quite embarrassed about this.

BLACK WEARING BLACK-MASK: Oh, I'm sorry.

WHITE WEARING WHITE MASK: Yes, it's, well, really *quite* embarrassing. I don't care, you understand, but I live in a neighborhood where we have . . . it's so hard to explain . . . where we have *points.*

BLACK WEARING BLACK MASK: You have *what?*

WHITE WEARING WHITE MASK: I know it's complex and it sounds ridiculous, but we have points . . . somebody looking for a house to buy is given so many points on the basis of, well his race or his religion or . . . [*pause*] . . . and a colored man doesn't have many points, enough points . . . you see? This is really quite embarrassing. I'm terribly sorry. But you see why I had to ask . . .

BLACK WEARING BLACK MASK: That wouldn't affect *me,* would it? I mean, I'm not colored, I'm black.

WHITE WEARING WHITE MASK: Well, as a matter of fact . . .

BLACK WEARING BLACK MASK: Oh, I see.

WHITE WEARING WHITE MASK: I just don't know what we're going to do about this race business. I think it's getting worse all the time. [*Lights start fading to total blackout.*] Just because of the color of a man's skin . . . [*He continues speaking in total blackout.*] . . . I mean, anybody can see you're black and I'm white. [*Then his voice becomes the voice of someone making a train station announcement over a loudspeaker, impersonal, obtrusive, maddeningly repetitive.*] Anybody can see you're black and I'm white, anybody can see you're black and I'm white, anybody can see you're black and I'm white, anybody can see you're black and I'm white anybody can see you're black and I'm white . . .

[*The lights come up and the actors are sitting on the stage but they have reversed their masks . . . the white actor once again wears a black mask and the black actor wears a white mask. They sit in silence as the curtain closes.*]

❧

Anna Higgs was an exceptionally bright, scrupulously honest, deeply religious and quite beautiful teen-age girl living on a farm in Iowa when she experienced her first vision. She saw God.

God, she told the religion editor of The Associated Press, was *not* dead, and, in fact, appeared to be an African, male, around fifty years of age, very black, and spoke in a broken accent which reminded her of "a foreign student attending Iowa State University" whom she had seen on TV.

Anna Higgs had two more visions, the first one three months later, the final one seven months after that. In the second vision, she met God's wife, an attractive woman who seemed to be in her twenties, was light complexioned with blonde hair,

and spoke "in an upper-class English accent."
Finally, in her third vision—which God told her
would be the last—she was introduced to God's
children, a teen-age boy and a young girl, as well
as his brother and sister-in-law ("they looked
Spanish") and received from God the Sixty
Sacred Scrolls on which she founded her new religion.

The Prayer Faith, as she named it, contained
surprisingly contradictory elements. The Sixty
Sacred Scrolls incorporated principles of the new
morality with severely primitive dietary regula-
tions. The result was that P.F.'s, as members of
the religion were known, found themselves with
extreme sexual freedom yet were unable to eat
meat on three full days out of each week.

The religion soon had grassroots women
leaders known as priestesses, yet not long afterward there was a global head who was male. He
was given the title of Mandator and this office was
initially filled by Anna Higgs' brother, John
Higgs, who moved from his rural Iowa farm to a
building in Des Moines which later became the
Mandatorium.

Because of mass communications, word of the
Prayer Faith spread quickly. It swept across
Africa, rapidly supplanting all other religions,

❧

and was very popular in South America where special devotions in Spanish were offered to God's brother and sister-in-law.

Prayer became highly stylized, following a new God Alphabet which was included in the Sixty Sacred Scrolls. This led immediately to an official Prayer Wheel which could be used equally well in Buenos Aires and Berlin, New Delhi and Chicago, Johannesburg (where the faith was initially underground) and Sydney. The Prayer Wheel, by utilizing the God Alphabet, remained uniform across all national and linguistic boundaries. Prayer became a form of conversation with God and his family. Members of different nations, because of their strong bond mutually cemented by using the Prayer Wheel, refused to take up arms against each other and world peace first became a distinct possibility.

Population control also loomed as a foreseeable reality when, in every part of the world, families wished to pattern themselves after God's family which consisted of two children. In fact, one of the few violent aspects of the Prayer Faith consisted in some cruelly repressive actions taken against families having more than two offspring.

The family unit was also changing form. Because God's brother and sister-in-law lived, according to Anna Higgs, in the same house with God, his wife and children, families throughout the world were revising traditional structures. Now brothers and sisters, with *their* families, were all moving together under a single roof. Too, a more cosmopolitan element was entering into family life. An Indian man looked for a Pakistani wife, a Frenchman sought a German mate, a black African man automatically thought of marriage in connection with a white British woman. The power of the Union of South Africa, already morally shattered, had now received an economic *coup de grâce,* with the once-proud country petitioning the United Nations for assistance as "a disaster area."

Racism in the U.S. diminished as Prayer Wheels, based on conversations with the black God and his lovely young white wife, replaced television sets. As the Prayer Faith quickly accomplished results of what segments of Christianity had tried in vain to do under the name "social action," religion changed, becoming more and more interior or meditative. The conversations with God and his family were intensely personal. People spent hours each day in such conversations, preferring them to human verbal encounters. Dope in all forms nearly vanished, along with cigarettes and social consumption of alcohol. This was not due to any strain of puritanism in the Prayer Faith but rather because people did not wish to be distracted from clear and total concentration in prayer.

Inevitably there were schismatic attempts to corrupt or exploit the Prayer Faith. One such attempt was originated by a small group of black supremacists who stated their thesis simply on the basis of God's being black. Therefore, social equality among races was ungodly, they said, as only black supremacy could reflect pure godliness. This movement attracted a brief flurry of attention in the ghettos of New York, Detroit, Cleveland, Chicago, Washington, Newark, and Philadelphia, as well as parts of Africa, but the integrative qualities of the Prayer Wheel eventually let to a world-wide demand that it be officially declared heretical.

A severe danger to the Prayer Faith emerged when a group of theologians claimed that God was a Duality. This position, originating in San Francisco, affirmed belief that God was "one Person" but "two people," namely God and his wife. Their differences in sex, color, and language, representing two quite different people, were made a "holy unity" in the "one, indivisible, eternal Person of

❧

God." A group of theologians in Paris quickly supported this view. Oxford and Cambridge attacked it angrily and a world-wide religious dispute seemed inevitable. Then the Mandator announced that "only God is God," introducing a human analogy to the effect that the male is the only head of a family and household. While this announcement was greeted coldly by dependent mothers in urban centers, and by strong adherents to the feminine mystique, it was generally accepted as plausible and soon became a cornerstone of faith: "only God is God, and only God's wife is God's wife." No one made a further issue out of this dispute for the reason that prayer included conversations with God *and* his wife.

The most difficult schismatic response to the Prayer Faith emerged in the form of strongly nationalistic and also puritanical movements which sprang up, more or less simultaneously, in Ireland, the Canadian Province of Quebec, the American state of Texas, and nations once belonging to the Austro-Hungarian Empire. The Separatists, as they were called, wished to be identified along highly individualistic lines instead of merely as P.F.'s. Consequently, the Prayer Wheel was in danger of modification in these areas to conform to cultural mores. The dissidents all found their leaders in former Christians, who had a long tradition of tribal (American, French, German, English, Latin, *or* Anglo-Saxon) gods, as well as a highly superstitious practice of "magic prayer" and a double-standard morality.

As a matter of historical interest, the most virulently schismatic of these bodies was located in Texas. Obsessed by a pathological need to be individualistic, the P.F.'s there became highly cultic. Texans kept their Prayer Wheels but wished to add to their devotions an element no one else shared. This took the form of handling snakes in divine worship.

Where the Prayer Faith had been marked by decentralization, the Texan schismatics now began to find a new focus in building-centeredness. The Prayer Faith practiced the concept of One Altar, this being symbolized by the existence of the Mandatorium. Now, in Texas, there emerged a heretical obsession with many altars located in many buildings separated from each other, at first by cultic practices alone, soon by cultural, economic, and social divisions. In one location, anti-Semitism was discovered as a basis of separated structures, in another anti-Methodism, both of these having reverted to pre-heresies.

Snake handling achieved international notori-

ety in Dallas, then spread to Fort Worth and
Houston. A strong anti-snake handling counter-
movement firmly kept it out of San Antonio. At
the height of the schism, crateloads of snakes were
being imported into Texas, the local supply and
that of neighboring states having been totally
exhausted. Highly individualistic schools of snake
handling came into being as the movement itself
fragmented. Some preferred brightly colored
snakes to black ones, others had preferences as to
sizes, places of origin, and the factor of safety in
handling various snakes. A Dallas suburb had
even turned to cobras at the height of the
movement.

Disasters in Texas places of worship, coupled
with a massive international Prayer Faith re-
pudiation of snake handling as a separatist cultic
practice heretically attacking the One Altar concept, brought the movement to its demise. However, repercussions would be felt for many years
within the Prayer Faith as a result of scars and ill-
feeling.

Indeed, the ultimate decline of the Prayer Faith
as a major world religion had its origins in these
schismatic movements. This was because, in an
effort to prevent such happenings in the future,
the Mandator consolidated his power and estab-

lished the beginnings of a hierarchy. He appointed Sub-Mandators, all of whom reported directly to him, in twenty world capitals. Then he called a Prayer Faith Fair, to assemble in Moscow. This was a move of unprecedented importance, consolidating the Prayer Faith's success in communist nations. In China, it had been reported to the Mandator that a translation of the Sixty Sacred Scrolls had recently surpassed the sayings of Mao, while Cuba and Albania had requested personal visits inside their borders by the Mandator and his chief aides.

Shortly before the great Prayer Faith Fair, to be held in Moscow, Anna Higgs died in Iowa. She had become a legend in her lifetime, refusing to leave the farm which was already a shrine. Anna Higgs had stedfastly declined to intervene in administrative concerns of the Prayer Faith and seldom even journeyed to the Mandatorium near her home. Her death would become a turning point in the Prayer Faith, an event marked by political manipulation and ensuing bitter controversy.

The Mandator seized upon Anna Higgs' death as a primary weapon in his fight to hold tight reins of authoritarian control over the Prayer Faith. In Moscow, the Prayer Faith Fair commenced with a gigantic memorial service dedicated to Anna Higgs. The Mandator, accompanied by the twenty Sub-Mandators, marched in a procession watched by 800,000 people there and millions on world-wide television. Prayer Wheels were put aside as all attention focused on this event. Invoking Anna Higgs' memory, the Mandator placed the greatest stress on the Sixty Sacred Scrolls, emphasizing obedience and central authority over regional autonomy and informal conversations with God and his family.

This initiative momentarily strengthened the position and authority of the Mandator, yet it signaled long-range opposition rooted in orthodox reaction. This opposition would remain underground for the present. Its clandestine quality would become a primary cause of its ultimate power.

Seeking to consolidate his gains, and to establish the office of Mandator as all-powerful, the Mandator now prepared to launch a propaganda effort of unprecedented scope and psychological intensity. Turning toward the world of advertising, publicity, and mass communications, the Mandator felt uneasy. He would be on strange new ground.

He decided that his guide and mentor should be

Jane Webb, the young woman who had founded
the already famed advertising agency Webb,
Ogilby & Bernbad. In only a few years she had
revolutionized many advertising concepts, having
taken virtually unknown accounts and built them,
rapidly and spectacularly, to positions of emi-
nence. Jane Webb came to the Mandatorium for
their first meeting.

The Mandator liked her combination of youthful enthusiasm (she was in her early thirties) and
cool professional detachment. She would do a
good job, not only because she was a pro, but for
the sake of her own success image. Quite honestly
she told the Mandator that she was not in any
sense a religious person. Yes, she had dabbled
briefly in the Prayer Faith, but her whole concern
and strength had been channeled into the organization of Webb, Ogilby & Bernbad. The Mandator
said he understood perfectly.

The Mandator told Jane Webb that her work on
the God image would be all-important. Despite the
location of the Mandatorium inside the United
States, the God image must never be "American"
but always "international." Whenever a sense of
the transcendental was attached to God, this must
never be translated as remote or uninvolved.
"The God image," he said, "is warm, friendly,

and like a *good* friend." Jane Webb told him this was the way she always thought of God.

The Mandator explained that God had now decided formally to place his seal of approval on the Prayer Faith, which would, after this occasion, henceforth be considered *God's* religion. It would now be the only faith. In fact, in obedience to God's wishes, the Prayer Faith would soon launch, for the first time in its history, a missionary program. God wanted everybody to be a P.F. In this way, God's purposes for earth could be greatly accelerated.

What, Jane Webb asked the Mandator, were God's purposes?

He replied that God had decided human beings should become more religious. If they did, they could increasingly be on the same wave length as God and respond, more or less automatically and without effort or trouble, to what he thought would be best for the earth on a day-to-day basis. To simplify matters of God's relations with humans, the Mandator would from now on act as a mediator between them. He would act as God's man, or representative, on earth.

Now, the Mandator continued, it was precisely at this point that public relations and advertising counsel were sorely needed. This was for the reason that God had previously worked more personally with individual human beings. The concept of man's creation with a free will had always been a central one. Nor were these being fundamentally altered. There was only to be a change of emphasis. From now on, the Mandator would stand in a new relationship to God, *interpreting* his wishes for human beings.

Jane Webb said that the full staff and facilities of Webb, Ogilby & Bernbad would be put to work on the account immediately. But she already had her slogan which would be transmitted to the public through all media: "God is *Good*. Good is *God*. Find Good God in the Prayer Faith *Now*." The Mandator was most pleased.

Jane Webb returned to New York. Soon other members of Webb, Ogilby & Bernbad began arriving at the Mandatorium for conferences. Jane Webb personally supervised the account, spending every other week in Iowa. She set up advertising schedules for each of the twenty capitals throughout the world where Sub-Mandators were stationed.

She suggested a subtle nationalizing of God's image. Let him, in Asia, appear somewhat more Asian (while, of course, remaining essentially himself). On the same basis, *suggest* a French

God for Frenchmen, a Mexican God for Mexicans, a Swedish God for Swedes. Such deviations, to be found in a certain nationalizing of the God image, could be more than counteracted by affirming a rigid orthodoxy in the context and form of the Prayer Wheel. This, along with the new role of the Mandator, could serve as unyielding elements of centralized unification.

Webb, Ogilby & Bernbad devised twelve points for the Prayer Faith missionary program. It must eschew controversy at all times. By taking its claims completely for granted, it would refuse to engage in debate or any kind of argument with "other" so-called faiths. All missionaries must be married and have two children. It was suggested that there be a definite nationalistic approach in the assignment of missionaries—so, a Japanese family would work for the Prayer Faith in Japan, a Chilean in Chile, a Scottish in Scotland. This meant that missionary training centers, which should be under the strictest Mandatorium control, would nonetheless have to be set up in widely separated areas on all continents. Jane Webb worked out in minutest detail a plan which would guarantee ideological non-deviationism coupled with geographical disparity.

Not wishing to raise again the specter of theological debate centered around the feminine mystique, Jane Webb nevertheless proposed strengthening the image of God's wife. *"Two* are better than one," she told the Mandator. Priestesses and wives of the Mandator and Sub-Mandators were to relate more closely to God's wife than to God, while, at the same time, never forgetting the accepted dictum "Only God is God, and only God's wife is God's wife."

The image of the Mandator came under scrutiny by Webb, Ogilby & Bernbad. By virtue of the past isolation of the office, there had been no clear pattern of marriage and family structure among Mandators. Some had even remained celibate, the administrative demands of the office being so time-consuming. Now, the agency suggested a definite, unalterable pattern of marriage (interracial) and family structure (two children) for the Mandator.

The present Mandator was black and unmarried. It was acknowledged this situation should be changed without undue delay. Three months later, Jane Webb and the Mandator were married before 300,000 P.F. delegates in Stockholm. The Prayer Faith became a permanent account of Webb, Ogilby & Bernbad. Jane Webb, as senior partner, moved the agency's main office from New York to Des Moines.

∼

Inevitably, it was seen later, a "Mother Jane" cult grew up around her. Women in every part of the world came to identify with Jane more than with the Mandator. Administratively, this eased his burdens for she could make a tour of women's P.F. organizations and leave him behind at the Mandatorium to catch up on paper work. Jane became intensely religious, spending several hours each day in conversation with God's wife on the Prayer Wheel.

Soon Jane assumed control over the P.F. missionary training program, becoming the most widely traveled woman in the world. She introduced bright new colors in Prayer Wheels and commissioned top designers in each country to create smart and colorful dresses for priestesses.

The Sixty Sacred Scrolls had to be updated in the interest of "relevance and contemporaneity," Webb, Ogilby & Bernbad informed the Mandatorium. A high-level commission was appointed by the Mandator to undertake this task. Simultaneously, a massive campaign was launched to "enlist youth" in the Prayer Faith, for an anti-religion movement was becoming prominent on university campuses. Youth evangelists were to be given special instruction in missionary training centers. It was felt such evangelists should play the guitar, study students' speech and dress patterns, and be well-grounded in the rapidly changing sex mores of the emergent neo-puritanism found in the younger generation.

This neo-puritanism asserted itself in a dramatic resurgence of fundamentalistic Christianity. One saw "Jesus Saves" painted on highway signs and scrawled on city walls. Architecture took a new interest in old Christian churches, making them a very fashionable symbol for the avant-garde. Soon one heard updated old Christian hymns, these becoming sensationally popular among youth when sung traditionally with only organ accompaniment.

Jane Webb realized too late that the Prayer Faith had become overidentified with the Establishment. An intellectual, student, and avant-garde reaction against it had set in. On December 25, Christmas and Hanukkah were being widely observed as they had not been in decades. One could dismiss this as mere protest but Jane realized it reflected a much deeper rise of feeling. It was Webb, Ogilby & Bernbad's job to discover the roots of this feeling.

Psychological depth surveys showed a public desire to have a "remote, distant, transcendent" God and a religion "separated from everyday

life.'' A clear majority of people did not want ''to
pattern our lives on God's life'' and expressed
doubt that ''anyone on earth understands anything about God's life.'' This amounted to a stun-
ning rejection by most people of Anna Higgs'
three religious visions.

The Mandator was told by the agency that the
results of the survey could be kept confidential for
perhaps three months. During this period, the
Prayer Faith would be in the enviable position of
knowing precisely what the public thought about
God and religion, while the public would not know.
After three months, however, the Prayer Faith
might be in utmost danger of dying out if it could
not, during the period, regain its original primitive and unalloyed appeal to the masses.

Lights in the Mandatorium burned for three
successive nights as discussions feverishly ensued. Where had the Prayer Faith failed? A Sub-
Mandator from China said that the ''pure faith''
of Anna Higgs had been ''corrupted'' by over-
centralized authority in the Mandatorium, wide-
spread heresies, arrogant antiecumenism and self-
perpetuation, and selling out to techniques of
mass communications as ''mere gimmicks.'' A
youth leader from Peru claimed the central
leadership of the Prayer Faith had become

"Elmer Gantrys in gray flannel suits," alluding to the role of Webb, Ogilby & Bernbad in the faith's evangelism. A powerful spokesman from Dallas, a descendant of a snake handler, angrily spoke of "betrayal of ideals."

However, a course had been set in motion by the Mandatorium and it would require much more time than the given three months to reverse it. Consequently, it was decided that the immediate changes must be public relations, rather than actual, ones. Committees were appointed to establish long-range changes, but these were seen as less urgent.

A key slogan, suggested by the agency, and adapted by the Mandatorium, was: "Don't Talk to God. Be Silent with the Good One. *Meditate with God.*" Every medium of communication was used to change public opinion concerning the nature of prayer. Implicit in the crash program was the obsolescence of the Prayer Wheel. No one in the Mandatorium failed to realize the dangers inherent in this development. Now the central unifying factor of the faith, beset by heresies and strong nationalistic influences, had suddenly been removed. The prestige of the Sixty Sacred Scrolls had, in fact, rested primarily in the final analysis on the Prayer Wheel.

The office of the Mandator remained alone as
the symbol of unity. Yet there was an evident
credibility gap between the office and the people.
It was the consensus of the Sub-Mandators and
influential youth leaders representing every part
of the world that a new Mandator be elected immediately as a means of dramatizing reform as
well as channeling new ideas. The Mandator accepted this, along with appointment as Mandator
Emeritus in charge of Berlin. Jane Webb would
accompany him to Germany and her partners
would assume direct supervision of the account
for Webb, Ogilby & Bernbad. However, it was
understood that the agency would play a subsidi-
ary role, stressing implementation rather than
decision-making.

The new Mandator had previously been based
in Rio de Janeiro. One of the youngest men among
the Sub-Mandators, he was married to a former
medical technician from Calcutta and they had
two children. He personally preferred silent
prayer to the practice of contemporaneous conversations with God based on the stylized alphabet of the Prayer Wheel. However, pointing out to
the Prayer Faith leadership that silent prayer or
meditation requires great personal discipline, he
announced eight "Arts of Discipline" which

might help in effecting among the masses a wholly new understanding of prayer.

Despite the obvious sincerity, enthusiasm, and decidedly youthful image of the new Mandator, the Prayer Faith simply could not regain its former position in the trust and devotion of the world's masses. The role of the Mandator itself was clearly not sufficient as a means of instigating unity among so many millions of scattered people. The Prayer Wheel had provided a clear and cohesive focus which the practice of silent prayer, never widely accepted, could not emulate. Religious anarchy replaced the former universal sense of well-being under the God whom Anna Higgs had seen in her visions.

The Mandatorium was now a quite modest operation in comparison with its previous splendor. Reform had installed in all key positions extremely fervent young men, true believers and social idealists who worked unceasingly for human betterment. However, despite their efforts, racism loomed as an ugly spirit once again while nationalism entered a bullish reactionary phase.

Ironically, members of other religious faiths, Marxists, and atheists alike increasingly revered Anna Higgs as a humanistic saint. Her old farm in Iowa far surpassed the Mandatorium in popu-

❧

lar favor and prestige. An eternal light burned at her grave in the farmland and thousands of people, a majority of them students, paid homage there annually.

What *had* Anna Higgs seen? This question was asked by youth in many lands. Finding it impossible to conceptualize God, they could not follow Anna Higgs into her segregated ghetto of metaphysics. But her simple belief stirred admiration. There was also a longing which, though it could seldom be articulated, found expression in honoring her.

They stood in the Iowa field, thousands of young people, looking at Anna Higgs' grave and seeing, not a father, but a mother.

Malcolm Boyd
ARE YOU RUNNING WITH ME
JESUS?   NS30   95¢

Vine Deloria, Jr.
CUSTER DIED FOR YOUR SINS   W213 $1.25

Joan Baez
DAYBREAK   N219   95¢

David Harris
GOLIATH   N332   95¢

Studs Terkel
DIVISION STREET: AMERICA   J105 $1.50
HARD TIMES: An Oral History of
the Great Depression   J109 $1.50

Coretta Scott King
MY LIFE WITH MARTIN
LUTHER KING, JR.   J100 $1.50

Jorge Luis Borges
THE BOOK OF IMAGINARY
BEINGS   QS19 $1.45

Richard Burgin
CONVERSATIONS WITH
JORGE LUIS BORGES   DS15 $1.65

William Robert Miller
GOODBYE, JEHOVAH   QS9 $1.45

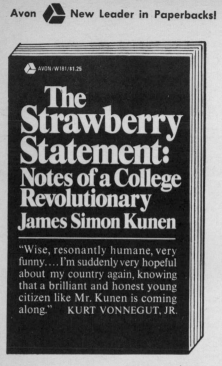